9781913111267

My Mind to Me a Kingdom Is

PAUL STANBRIDGE

GALLEY BEGGAR PRESS

First published in 2022
by Galley Beggar Press Limited
Norwich NR2 3LG

Text design and typesetting by Tetragon, London
Printed in the UK by CPI Group, UK

Paperback: 978-1-913111-26-7
Limited edition: 978-1-913111-25-0

My minde to me a kingdome is,
such perfect joy therin I find,
That it excells all other blisse,
which God or Nature hath assign'd.
Though much I want, that most would have,
yet still my mind forbids to crave.

No princely port nor welthie store,
no force to winne a victorie,
no wyly wit to salve a sore,
no shape to winne a loving eye:
to none of these I yeld as thrall,
for why my minde despise them all.

I see that plentie surfeits oft,
and hastie clymbers soonest fall:
I see that such as are a loft,
mishap doth threaten most of all:
these get with toyle and keepe with feare,
such cares my minde can never beare.

I presse to beare no haughtie sway,
I wish no more than may suffice:
I doe no more than well I may,
look what I want my minde supplies,
loe thus I triumph like a King,
my minde content with any thing.

I laugh not at anothers losse,
nor grudge not at anothers gaine:
no worldly waves my minde can tosse,
I brooke that is anothers bane:
I feare no foe nor fawne on friend,
I loth not lyfe nor dread mine end.

My wealth is health and perfect ease,
and conscience cleere my chiefe defence,
I never seeke by brybes to please,
nor by desert to give offence:
thus doe I live, thus will I dye,
would all did so as well as I.

A note on the poem's authorship

The poem which begins 'My Mind to Me a Kingdom Is' was first published in a collection of lyrics set to music by William Byrd called *Psalmes, Sonets & Songs* in 1588. Before this the poem had circulated Elizabeth I's court in manuscript form, as was the convention at the time. Publication was viewed by courtiers as little more than an irrelevance: if it was not vulgar, it conferred no merit on a work.

Always a popular lyric, from the middle of the nineteenth century the authorship of 'My Mind to Me a Kingdom Is' has been without exception attributed to the courtier Edward Dyer, a protégé and friend of Sir Philip Sidney. Dyer manoeuvred himself into the Elizabethan court under the patronage of the Earl of Leicester, though only under the condition of forfeiting a large proportion of his estate. After several years, Dyer fell out of the queen's favour for some undiscoverable reason and was exiled from the court to live on his Woodstock estate. Here, with no possibility of being granted a royal warrant, he was forbidden to trade, and so had to live off a meagre income from his rents. These, in turn, he was forced to share with the caretaker of Woodstock, one Henry Lee, whom the queen appears to have appointed by spite to occupy that position. These circumstances offer a convincing context for the writing of the poem by the spurned poet. Indeed, when the reader considers this context, the self-satisfied generalisations of the poem become gilded with a touching resonance. Behind the words is a newly palpable sense of the suffering of the individual who wrote them.

In an article published in the *Review of English Studies* in November 1975, however, Stephen W. May argues convincingly that Edward Dyer may not have been the author of the poem at all. Using evidence from all the extant manuscript versions of the poem, May concludes that it is more likely that Edward de Vere, Earl of Oxford, wrote the poem. Accordingly, all the poignant significance which had welled up inside the poem in consideration of Dyer's life immediately drains away.

CAVES

It was at a particularly difficult period of my life, one which I continue to find myself unable to look at directly, that I first began to develop an interest in the toponymy of the North Sea. A previous piece of work had involved my going through as many of the early maps featuring the British Isles as I could find, from the second century Ptolemaic, through the *mappae mundi* of the Middle Ages, to those of Caxton and his contemporaries in the Renaissance, and further, into the Enlightenment, the time of the great instruments, when the land mass, I noted, like a developing child in the womb begins to assume a shape with which we are familiar, one recognisably our own. What I was then pursuing, I cannot remember. But certainly, at that time, I was interested in what, to our thinking, is there: the land. It was only later, when that great shock befell me, that I first began to conceive of a greater attraction to the waters between.

Day by day, I downloaded more and more maps of the North Sea, and very soon was struck by an impression that we humans cannot refrain from naming things, that everything that is – and even isn't – must eventually accrue a denotative tag, even the shifting waters and unguessable floor of the ocean, as those mysterious names of the regions of the North Sea attest: Dogger Bank, Farn Deeps, Utsira High, Revet, Broad Fourteens, Devil's Hole, and so on. Nothing, I understood, was beyond the limitless power of words to name it: not the unseeable ground; not the shapeless water which, continually mingling and separating, is only ever itself in a single moment; not even the infinite extension of blank space above us – so like an ocean – and, within it, those great concentrations of gravity at the centre of which light is held still and time is said to stop, or not yet to have begun.

From a simple starting point, an innocent budding of the intellect, there may ensue a dogged, all-consuming undertaking which depletes the body, overstrains the senses and destroys the mind.

I can clearly recall the moment at which this interest in the names of the North Sea began. I was quickly scrolling through my library of images of historic maps – I believe it had to have been quickly, or else the effect would never have occurred – and as I did so the borderline of land and water as it made this sea on each map hopped and lurched in shape from one image to the next as if the sea were a living creature under the force of some paroxysm emerging from within itself. The name of this expanse of water, though, remained the same: there was a solidity – and a comfort in that solidity – to the wide-spaced placement of one letter after another across each blue expanse: NORTH SEA. The name, it is true, mutated in shape, position and size from one map to another, but still the sea was so much the North Sea that the words required no reading. But solidity, and comfort in solidity, is only understood when it is under threat of being taken away. Thus the ground was prepared for an aberration: on one of the maps the sea was denominated GERMAN OCEAN. It leapt off the screen in a shocking act of defamiliarisation. My initial assumption, that the conflict of the First World War must be responsible for the renaming – one, moreover, presented thus in the slender research into the matter – was quickly disproved by the most cursory glance at these maps' dates of production, the 'North Sea' being the denomination, I noted, on at least two mid-nineteenth-century maps.

And so it was that I began to collect these maps in earnest, and to look into their ways with names, to seek a story or a sense to the movement of time, which must be the same thing. I interrogated my database as if it were an ancient text which promised to disclose the greatest mysteries of the world, and returned to the maps, moving back step by step. Back I went, from Ernst Debes in 1876, through Bartholomew's *Times* maps of the 1860s, through the maps of Stielers, Petermann, Berghaus, back through Teesdale and maps made for Mitchell's *School and Family Geography* series, both in 1840, through Gilbert's in 1838 and Thomas Moule's the year before. Back I went, through John Cary's attractive presentation of 1811, through an anonymous map produced to commemorate the Franco-Russian treaties made at Tilsit in 1807, back through a 1749 Anglicised copy of Homann's Nuremberg production, whose representation of Britain and Ireland, with part of Holland, Flanders and France, it was pleased to describe as being 'agreeable to modern history'. Even in Thomas Bowles' plagiarised 1732 version of Herman Boll's original that expanse of water was denominated 'The British or North Sea' a full 150 years earlier than the academics describe the shift taking place. It was only upon reaching Robert Morden's maps of the first decades of the eighteenth century, published in Camden's *Britannia*, that the name change became observable. Morden's 1695 map designates it 'Germanicus Oceanus', while his 1722 map carries the legend 'The English or German Ocean'. Ten years later

Bowles calls it 'The British or North Sea', and we arrive at the present habit for naming that watery mass.

Had I been capable of observing myself more clearly at that time, I might perhaps have found it reasonable to clear away all these maps, close the many dozens of tabs in my browser, shut my notebooks, to cease generating and turning over and through vast quantities of data as if they were those waters themselves. In fact, it would be true to say that within only a few hours I had gathered enough information to make a persuasive case, against the untenable argument of the academics, that it was the Hanoverian accession of 1714 rather than the war of two centuries later that was the cause of this alteration. Why, if I had my answer, then, did this task preoccupy me for many months further? This general truth – that the renaming of the North Sea was a gradual process tentatively initiated in reaction to the politics of the early eighteenth century – was not enough. It was not enough because it did not *satisfy*. I pursued this new interest as if I were a plant and it were the sun: relentlessly, somatically, and under the force of a desire which swept every other consideration into irrelevance. And so how could something so impoverished as an answer cause me to cease this undertaking? It could not.

Even as I worked, I knew that I drew further back from my aim – whatever that might have been. I extended and deepened my database of antique maps, read every article I could find on Anglo-German relations in the eighteenth and nineteenth centuries, studied the long cartographic tradition linking Britain and Germany, phoned leading researchers in maritime history at universities and research institutions all round the world, and yet the true and inner meaning behind this toponymic shift from 'German Ocean' to 'North Sea' drew further and further back from my view. It is only now that I can observe myself at that time and understand that the answer I was looking for, far from being the initial and particular spark of this alteration, was in fact the very recession of sense though these layers of information away from my comprehension. I had made of myself an engine of distraction.

When night came, I put away my work, ate a little if I remembered, and then took myself to bed, where I would lie down and surge through the dark waters of a now nameless mass, always down, down through the plaited currents, down into the motionless fist-strong salted heaviness of it, down through the layers of sediment, marl, clay and rock, until, eventually, I found that cave which I had prepared without knowing for myself, one which the geology of the North Sea bed declares must be impossible – and yet here I am nevertheless – and in which, when lying there within its enclosure, I discovered there to be no necessity of sleep. A vast ocean of insomnia swelled up around me and I entered it willingly, with an avid hunger for that silent nightlong wakefulness which under normal circumstances would be intolerable.

★

At some indistinct point of my investigation the true pip and point to the reason for the change of the German Ocean to the North Sea ceased to be my concern, replaced as it was with a more specific inquiry – even if a more scattered and less quantifiable one – into the individual people who had made these maps and the relationships they held with the regions they sought to represent, all conducted in a final stage and with a growing sense – one which I now see to have been incontestably pathological – that if I could uncover the full and minute history of these forgotten lives, some amorphous form of redemption might be allowed to take place, though whether for me or for them I could not say.

I read of Heinrich Berghaus, and of Justus Perthes, the firm which published the maps he made with unparalleled attention to detail. I read of Alexander Keith Johnston, a partner in an

Edinburgh publisher which in 1848 bought the rights to Berghaus' maps. I read of how the engravers, receiving copies of the German plates, made tracings of the place nameplates, and converted each name – where it had been changed – back into its native form on a fresh piece of burnished copper. Looking at each map, I wondered about the interior life of its engraver – where and in what form, now, were the thoughts which had been produced by the engine of that brain? I read of August Petermann, Berghaus' protégé, and his visit to Edinburgh and London, where he stayed for nearly a decade from 1845 on, and how he caught the attention and acquired the devotion of a young John Bartholomew Jr, only sixteen years old when they first met. Later, after Petermann divorced, married again, and finally gave it all up in 1878 by shooting himself in the head, Bartholomew had a bust made of his industrious hero, which he displayed in the boardroom of the firm his father had established, and which was still there a hundred years after his death, though now has gone. We humans are like planets, and the motion we present in the world, though its ultimate cause be what is exterior to ourselves, is a corollary of the deeper, stronger and faster motion at our cores. Petermann, it seems, fell into that same affliction which creeps into us all, except that it was beyond his forbearance: a slowing beyond tolerance of the spinning at the centre of oneself. He found that nothing good could come of it, felt the spin wind down, and all that he had held to be in orbit of him drifted off to find some new star and moons and be left without light or tide.

I read into the deepest creases of these forgotten lives until there was nothing more to discover because all other traces had been lost. I felt a pull, a gravitational desire, to leap across from the known to the unknown, to discover the inner secrets of the dead and make solemn record of them, just as a child's desire to exhibit a found pebble or shell to parents is so serious and clear.

This being an impossibility, however, I sought meaning, as many do, by looking for origins, not knowing then what I know now: that historical origins are as chimerical and problematic as the inner thoughts of the dead.

I began to look further back into the history of map-making of this region, seeking in all probability a universal solution to the mess of existence which troubled me all the day long. In Herodotus' map of the world, made c.450 BC, I found organised the peoples and places of Europe, under unfamiliar names, on an unrecognisable physical mass of land about or within a sea of chaos. Here, before Rome, there is no Britannia or Germanicus, no Teutones, Angles, Saxons, Jutes, Vikings, Franks, and so on, only Celtae, Ligyes, Sigynnae, Eneti and Getae, found in this Roman copy of Herodotus in their later Latinate forms – already the names for things are being threshed through competing empires. In this early time, at the very beginning of history, the world is a strange shape: it huddles its land masses together at the centre, as if in fear, and is engulfed by the waters of multiple seas and oceans. It is in Pliny, Tacitus and Ptolemy in the first and second century that we first discover ourselves. In these accounts, and as it remained through the Middle Ages and Renaissance, Britain is separated from continental Europe by the 'Oceanvs Germanicvs', though in the medieval maps the earth has been turned ninety degrees by the power of Christ, cardinal orientation north is abandoned in favour of the east, and Jerusalem, the site of his wonderful self-immolation, is made the great navel of the world and its eschatological history, at least for a time.

One particular medieval map, found within a compilation of historical accounts called *La Mer des histoires*, and published in 1491, caught my attention. It presents the earth in the Isidoran T-O format which prevailed at the time, where the known world, its landmasses and seas, is surrounded and protected from the nameless blank space of the page upon which it is printed by a firm dark bounding line in a perfect circle; and where the seas – which go unnamed – pour out their source at the top of the illustration from a kind of walled spring, within which two men look with ambiguous purpose at one another across the dividing line created by the spine of the book, which runs as a fissure of vacant space through the centre of the earth between them. The brothers – how could I see these two men otherwise, after what had so recently happened with my own brother – stand within a walled enclosure above the Inde, beyond the eastern limit of the earth, and tend to the pouring of the seas out of their font down to the wretched human realm beneath, whose surface is covered only in cities, except where the pope resides. The devil is led by the hand by some unidentifiable personage, and two human-faced flowers are enwreathed by the water's threads. The two angelic brothers eye one another at their task, and who can

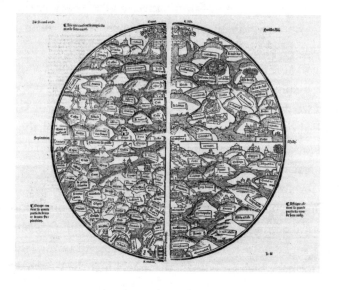

say if they are not in fact corporeal forms, ordinary men, engaged in mutual admiration, or devotion, or even suspicion that the other seeks not to water but rather drown the world and thus also himself, his rival?

This map was just one of many diversions which I was led to pursue, and which, taken in totality, were as intertwined, though purposeless and impenetrable, as the ribbons of water they neglected to try to represent. Looking back now on the manner and extent to which the waters of the German Ocean came to consume me – I do not believe this to be an overstatement – it seems impossible that it did not even occur to me that what I sought was not so much a subject in itself, a story to pursue, as a means of escaping the terror of looking at my own, in which, still, if I try to turn towards it, I discover only a blinding glare of terrible darkness which draws all words towards it and destroys them by the power of its gravitational pull. The naming of things, it is true, is no more than an attempt to subdue the terror of existence. Equally, though, hindsight has discovered for me that, whatever it is that preoccupies the thought and feeling, whether for good or bad, does in fact turn all eyes upon it, though under different forms or species, those interior eyes which we do not see with, or know, but which are most certainly there. Thus, what I avoided was precisely what I travelled towards, as, during those long insomniac nights, I flowed out like a river from this land of the living into the shifting waters and dwelt in a body of unobtainable insolidity. In truth, I was remaking myself and my world because the events of life had unpicked that which I had lived among, and that which I had until that time no cause to believe was unreal. Now there were only names, absences, gaps. Everything had melted into the watery elseness of the North Sea.

*

I circle, I do circle, and it is not within my remit to say if it is like the vulture around remains, or the wolf around its living prey, or the polecat, which returning from its own hunt circles the den which holds its cubs so as to check the territory for safety, never to lead the wolf or vulture back to the den to make prey of what is most precious. I cannot say what it is that I am circling, but it is true that I circle, I do – even down here, among the ribbons of water, deep within this cavern of rock.

After you were burned up and what had been you risen up the chimney to drift in the shapeless air, I walked out of the crematorium and saw your place marked with a name card and no wreath, because no one for shame can be allowed to see remnants of you, you who inhabit now your self-made box as ash. There rose in me the great urge to remove my two shoes and place them there in that absence, because somehow it was you that required them more for this new state of existence – you who chose not to wear shoes in the street even in life – and yet I didn't, and so no sign was made for your commemoration, not even one so temporary as that. So now, not knowing what such things as temporary and permanent can possibly mean in such matters as these, I discover I must make a sign.

I circle, and I ask questions, and I find that they are the same thing.

*

The obsession I had cultivated with the maps of the North Sea led me through numerous libraries and archives in South East England until it brought me to a collection in the Norwich Castle Museum – and, in particular, to a manuscript written by an unknown resident of that city between the two world wars – where that obsession was abruptly put to an end. This person's handwriting was poor, the script littered with crossings out and additions, and the pagination chaotic and disordered. (It is, according to the one I spoke with, a principle of archivists that the order of pages, even if disordered, is a feature of the archive, and should not be corrected – such a correction, indeed, is a movement away from truth rather than towards it.) Wearing white cotton gloves, feeling like a coroner of culture, I carefully turned these loose leaves, and instantly I saw how much there was of interest to me here. The identity of the author was unstated and unknown. There were no names, neither of people nor of places, and the time of writing was only indicated by the date ascribed to the archive which contained it. Yet here spoke a direct and unmediated voice, a true and real person, whose words, though their writer must now have been dead for a number of decades, came directly to me out of – where exactly? There is a great power held within the loops and folds of handwritten script. I felt a thrill of penetration which had eluded me in the search through the maps.

This person, in keeping with his or her place in the map library, held an interest in the cartography of the region. He or she had a vast collection of antique maps, and kept notebooks which functioned as a record of work undertaken with these maps as subject, but also of daily events such as occurred. In another context this would mostly have made for very dull reading indeed; but whether it was my own state of mind at the time, or something quite other, I hung on every word. Every weekday I walked through the city and round the walled mound of the castle to the old portcullis-like door which was opened to me by an assistant and by whom I was ushered into the frigid dark stone anteroom of the library. I stowed my coat and bag, collected the notebook I was working on, took my seat under the leaded window, pulled on the white cotton gloves, laid the long ribboned paperweight over the book's open pages, and read on. There was the occasional mention of walks and meals taken, domestic duties performed, thoughts on public life, but almost all of the space of the notebooks was dedicated to cartographic observations. Each new map acquired is recorded on a new line with asterisks at either end of its title. The general impression of reading the notebooks is a quotidian disordered smallness, like looking at worms at work in soil behind a plate of glass. However, at a certain point – with the earliest mention of one particular map – I began to experience an impression of a narrative thread emerging in the writing. The writer had ordered a number of maps from an antiquarian in the North somewhere, forgotten about them, and then was surprised several months later by their arrival by post, following a diversion through numerous sub-post offices across the country. Opening the roll, the author of the notebook discovered that one of the maps was a duplicate of one already owned. Nothing is recorded further in regard to this matter for a week, and it is only with hindsight that both the author and I the reader note how this duplicate map is beginning to take on a certain role. A detailed comparison of the two copies of this map of the North Sea is recorded for the first time in notebook 26 (as catalogued by the archivist), and by the end of that same notebook ten or so days later the two had evidently been pinned up beside one another. Imagine (writes the author, reminiscing about this moment of discovery several months later, in book 27) if I had sent the map back!

At some indeterminable time, the author of the notebooks begins to make more and more frequent assessments of these two copies of the map, and with more and more enthusiasm. 'Every morning,' as is written in the middle of Notebook 28, 'waking up in a fever for the day's work. Come into workspace, bring up blind, uncover mirror (my old & incurable conviction that uninhabited rooms should not have mirrors open to their vacancy, poor mother), full of fear that nothing has happened, but also that something has. Baffled.'

The entries from this point onwards become longer and more detailed, and full of references to an impenetrable code system to describe different regions of the two maps. The pages become increasingly dense with alphanumerical codings, sketches of emergent shapes and transcriptions of a kind of runic language. As in content, so likewise in form: the lineation in the notebook becomes less and less strict, until each page is a chaos of uninter-pretable signs scrawled over one another; one which ends abruptly in the latter part of Notebook 47, and following which there is only blank space for the remaining pages. From the evidence, it seemed that the author of these notebooks had conceived of some kind of livingness within one of the two maps, and descended quickly thereafter into insanity. Disappointed and somewhat chastened, I made agreement with myself that these researches of my own might for the sake of my health be suspended or at least curtailed, until I discovered a note inserted into the archive referring to the records for a Jan Baumgarten held in the Norwich

Borough Asylum archive. Of course, and against all the determination of my resolution just then made, I immediately phoned the Norfolk County Library Service in order to request access to this archive. It was here that I discovered that the author had been committed to the Asylum, though for blindness rather than mental incapacity, and that, no doubt under pressure of boredom as much as anything else, he had begun making a record of his life, presumably by dictation to a doctor or nurse at the hospital, who had typed the account up. He hurries through patches of his early life, omits whole decades of his youth and maturity, only giving us the odd paragraph on his love of sailing, the mischief he got up to with numerous young women in his travels during the War, and his move to England in the late 1920s, until he arrives at the maps. It is here that his true interests lie, and the Dutchman, in fussily elegant English, discloses the narrative which the notebooks held in code but which I was incapable of translating into meaningful words.

I quote the narrative in full:

It was at some point during a long period of hot windless weather that I noticed at the centre of the region of sea which formed the locus of my current interest a discolouration which, owing to the unseasonable heat, I would normally have not hesitated to ascribe to a reaction of the lignin in the wood pulp to the light, yielding those destructive blooms of acidity familiar from even such brief exposure to old books as is afforded by browsing in some old fusty bookshop. It is frequently the case that antique books and maps which have been stored since publication and appear to be utterly inviolate – objects which often astonish one by their capacity to transport us in mind back to the time of their production (it is not at all uncommon to discover the pages still uncut) – may, as soon as they are brought out of their long dwelt-in darkness into the light of our present day, find themselves subject to an immediate and rapid corruption, as if the light of our contemporary world was too much for their lack of sophistication (in the pejorative sense) to bear. I sprayed both maps with my preferred de-acidifying solution, and expected no worse to befall either.

Within not much time at all, however – several weeks at most – numerous fine lines became visible on the map in question and not the other, some apparently dotted, as if showing the route a passenger ferry might take, though all these routes were meandering and led nowhere at all; and, moreover, all of them remained confined to that area of sea between Britain, Norway, Denmark, Germany and Belgium within which the crooked legend 'THE NORTH SEA' was enclosed. In fact, I was intrigued to note how the network of lines, taken together, seemed to be concentrated around that area where Doggerbank lies beneath the surface. Under the scrutiny of a 40x magnifying glass, the situation only became more confounding. Each of the lines made upon the map was in fact composed of a multitude of little scratches, similar in kind if not in cause, it struck me, to those on the Hereford Mappa Mundi by which numerous Francophobes had demonstrated their predilections and defaced the city of Paris, for each ran if not in absolute parallel with the others – such a thing we are informed by the scientists has been shown against all right sense of judgment to be an impossibility – then at such an approximation to it as to insist even moreso the agency of a fallible human hand rather than the efficiency and uniformity of a machine. This was the first time that such a thought had occurred to me, and I present it now as if it seemed a definite possibility. At that time, as now, I believed there to be no such possibility of foul play. Howsoever another person might enter my locked study, within my own home, a home moreover which I so seldom left; and by what means that person might also be capable of knowing to concern him or herself with the representation of that area of ocean between the 50th and 60th parallel, from the meridian line to ten degrees east – in short the area with which I had been preoccupied for so long myself – I must admit to finding myself incapable of conceiving.

This was merely the beginning, however. The stitch-like lines which I believed to have begun appearing in the North Sea of this map soon appeared to complexify, to become more varied in structure and interrelation, as if they were the growing network of capillaries of an organism as it matures. I could not bring myself to pronounce this emerging set of marks as part of a system of scribed communication (I had not yet entirely lost all sense of proportion). Yet these marks, which, taken in totality, viewed at a distance – from the land so to speak – appeared to be the random results of the original copper plate having picked up scratches, patches of oxidization and other blemishes synonymous with a poor system of storage – a state of affairs which perhaps would account for the willingness of Justus Perthes to allow the plates to go to Bartholomew for a quarter of their value – appeared, when I brought my attention out into the ocean and down to a small area of its waters (to the location of the Witch Ground Graben as it abuts Canary Terrace, or of the highest hills at the western end of Dogger Bank, for example) to form discrete and intentioned entities from some manner of runic alphabet whose forms were now unknown and whose meaning was irretrievable.

In the ensuing weeks, the network complexified further, the threads meshed with each other like the capillaries of a mold which, having rapidly penetrated the full body of a fruit and found its resource of sustenance to be apparently inexhaustible, extends itself further from the surface in a cloud of decay, until the map was supplemented with an alternative account of reality, one which, as far as I knew, seemed by what could not possibly be accounted for by chance alone to accord with the reality beneath the waters to a far greater degree than that ordinarily presented even by such maps as concern themselves with the ocean floor. Indeed, the moraine of Dogger Bank swelled up out of the sea to become Doggerland once more, as if the intervening ten millennia had never occurred. The Devil's Hole sank down into a deeper obscurity. What now *was*, was embellished with what once had been, and inevitably would be in the long drag down into the future. Most interesting, though, were the waters themselves, that which no map seeks to represent, being to all intents and purposes for the mapmakers empty space, and which appeared in all the impossible complexity of their movement of mingling to be represented in the map's new and continuing work upon itself.

The apparent fragmented letter forms which I had observed changed from one day to the next, merged, crossed one another, only to emerge a week hence, sometimes the same, sometimes transformed. (The reader may consult my journal for a diagrammatic record of this part of the development of the map, should he or she desire to do so.) There was antagonism and even on occasion what one might describe as a manner of watery understanding, or so it appeared, to the flux of signs upon the map. Within a year of first noticing this efflorescence of signification – if that is what it might acceptably be termed – I seldom left the house except to obtain the bare essentials, and in fact confined myself to a single spot within this one room in order to observe the intricate developments which occurred within the shallow bowl of the North Sea. By the procurement of two ceiling-mounted Osram halophosphate lamps I was able to relieve some of the strain from my eyes, and yet by the same token, my working hours thereby greatly extended, my eyes began again to suffer with the effort of such long periods of close work. Although the quality of my vision did not at this time decline, I was beleaguered with sharp headaches and strains to the eyes which made me irritable and would have made me bad company if ever I had been in any such. I worked through this pain and discomfort and found my sufferings rewarded with observations of great arabesques of uninterpretable signs, swarms of runes and letter forms built out of one another in cycles of interpenetration up, down, round and over, so that what appeared to be at the top, the latest development, was invariably also at the bottom, underpinning the chrystalline shapes which emerged from it. Everything was – impossibly, tantalisingly, incontestably – both the source and outcome of its sibling others, flowing round and round like the water it represented.

It was in the eighth year of my observances that I first experienced a bout of sightlessness. I remember I had been paying particular attention to a constellation of heptangulate particles which had developed out of the eighth quadrant of Sector C4.2 – or so I had been urged by the quantity of data I by then had gathered to name the separate regions of my map – which, had the map shown such subaquatic features (which of course it couldn't, these having yet to be found sufficiently necessary of investigation at the time of the map's publication), was a little to the west of the Outer Silver Pit. I was expectant of a radical mutation at any moment, something I had not so far witnessed except in the retrograde, from the evidence of subsequent formations according to the caprices of these nameless forms. In short, I was in a state of perpetual excitement and agitation for an event continually deferred as the ocean was opening up like a galactic expanse into ever greater spatial extension, infinite space within finite bounds.

The original map, I should point out, had by this time become a mere foundation to the baroque structures which now grew up from its surface, like Chartres as it sprouted up from the flat plain of Normandy in the twelfth century, or the robust salt towers which have been growing out of Lake Urmia in Iran since a time far, far beyond. On the day in question, at approximately 2pm, an excruciating pain punched into the backs of my eyes and every scrap of the visible world was swept out of existence, everything around me turning not dark as the story goes but being engulfed in a shapeless swathe of bright light, as if the foamy waters of this sea were rising with resentment, a show of mastery, up around the sight which attempted to master them. During this period (these bouts at first only lasted for a quarter of an hour or so) it was not the loss of my sight per se which perturbed me, but the possibility that I would miss what it was I sought so ardently to observe, such was the rapidity with which the map was shifting its shape and growing out of itself. I was relieved, therefore, when my sight returned, dimly at first, to note that no dramatic changes had taken place during this period, and that the small holes in my data which had been opened up by this brief enforced hiatus would permit of being filled without too much guesswork. Nevertheless, there is always a perilous inexactitude to filling in the space between what was and what is.

These bouts of sightlessness, however, became longer; and, with time, increased in frequency; until it was not unusual for my scientific enquiry to be forced into suspension for more than half the day and night taken altogether. People who have pursued an ardent passion, whether in youth or no, may perhaps excuse the apparent cavalier attitude I exhibited in neglecting the care of my sight, comprehending as they surely will the force which drove me on. To those who have not, and so cannot, a word: I fear you have not lived.

In short, it was not two years hence, a mere ten years into my researches, and in spite of the introduction of certain precautionary measures meant to counteract such an eventuality – working in three hour shifts; resting the eyes with closure between; administering cold compresses to the temples between bouts of work; sighting a distant solitary tree for a time from the attic window (I do not mind admitting it invariably put me in mind of Golgotha and the Cross, except transposited to our cold and northerly climate, and not a tree of cypress or cedar, but of oak) – that I lost all semblance of sight, and live now permanently within the bright clear waters of blindness which have risen up around me.

*

Deep at the heart of things, time slows to a stop. This is why I am here and like this, held in this fleshy body, while you are now become only the formulae on the sheaves of paper which filled the container of your rooms like waters. There is a romance to becoming a black hole.

But what can lie at the centre of an undifferentiated mass? Perhaps some unimaginable crystal structure eternally forming in no-time. Has our earth grown a pip or seed, a veritable centre to itself, an axis, stump, root or omphalos? The scientists by cunning cross-threshment and combination of figured planes can see past the origin of the universe back before the bounce through the dark eye of our becoming in which time stopped, and they have tried to explain. Across billions of light years back in time through the channels of the fini-infinite mollusc, the uneternal holes, and down to the Planckton of being, the shortest possible thing, across which even light must crawl hideously in its journey. But you cannot look a little way into the ground. Nobody can know what is at the centre of us, whether seed or crystal, root or perhaps emptiness, as some nuts open up an airiness inside themselves in the vigour of their own growing.

Deep beneath the ocean, splashing about in our nickel bath, observing the spinning at the centre of this earth, I find that his voice comes not to or through me, but out of as it were myself, an inestimable thing: Each planet, moon, star makes a pulling of itself by hand of matter, by fist furled having centre to itself, like desire. Yes, everything you see and don't see around you is predicated upon desire. And so do not come to me with shoulds and shouldn'ts, because the sword is swung, desire ran through, and here I am, everywhere.

And when I wake up he is again gone.

*

It was during the return journey home from the Norwich Millennium Library, with a photocopy of this typescript in my bag, that I first felt a drag at my left side, in manner like gravity or a current of water, an undertow, one leaving me feeling frightened and faintly nauseous, that has since become a regular fixture in my neurophysiology. Lying on my bed that night, I again went down into the cold waters of the German Ocean which had claimed the sight of my new unknown friend. Down through the ribbons of its darkness, down, until I reached the silts and sands of its own bed. I burrowed like an eel, disturbed the dormant sediments, the grits and dusts which had been disgorged by the great rivers all around me: Rhine, Elbe, Glomma, IJssel, Meuse, Weser, Humber, Tay, Scheldt, Tweed, Thames – even, as I was to learn, the mighty Bytham, which had flowed out of the land mass we now know of as Norfolk, until it was abruptly erased from prehistory by the Anglian glaciation half a million years ago, though its sands still lie beneath those of its watery offspring, awaiting their next orogeny.

In view of my condition, what had recently happened, the attendant or consequent insomnia, the vertigo, the desire to be deep down there, it takes little effort to conject the cause of the attraction I felt for one particular feature of the seabed which for centuries, owing to its predilection for robbing trawlers of their nets, has been denominated the Devil's Hole. Did I not make my way down into its depths every night? By day, I sat in the library and undertook my researches.

In early investigations of the North Sea bed, dynamic positioning was most effectively made by use of a taut-wire lowered to the seabed, whose accuracy, even taking into account catenary deviation and the effect of current on the wire, has been proven to be surprisingly good. HMS *Fitzroy*, a surveying ship leaving Aberdeen one rainy morning in May 1930, ran back and forth above the trenches taking soundings, and, by use of all that could be found of solidity in that shifting realm – taut-wire, beacons and star-sightings – the positions and depths of these trenches of the deep sea were asserted to a hitherto unparalleled measure of accuracy. The normal gradient of the ocean floor – a single degree, it was discovered – is superseded here by a comparatively steep ten degrees at the location of the trenches. The mean depth in the surrounding area – a mere eighty to ninety metres – opens down, so far as the *Fitzroy* discovered in its investigation, to two hundred and thirty in the deepest part of the trench. The trenches, then, are not those tectonic types which are characterised by vertiginous drops into nothing, and which are liable to terrify the mind, but rather are – or were found by the *Fitzroy* to be – the gentle rise and fall of a pattern of silt, sand and dust deposition (predominantly quartzose with a subsidiary quantity of metamorphic rock fragments and heavy minerals) from the rivers to the west. This layer of loose material, it was later discovered by the drilling of a borehole at the edge of one of the trenches, is approximately ten metres deep, though much deeper at the deepest part of the trench. The trenches themselves, which would be far deeper and steeper had the river depositions not filled them in, have been formed in an undulating clay bed probably by river erosion when sea levels were much lower and this area of land, by the happenstance of geological development at the time, had not yet been forced down into a dip by the violence of the Alpine orogeny to be flooded by the sea, long after we – I mean here not myself so much as the landmass on which I live – had left the equator for good some 500 million years ago on Avalonia.

Developments in seismic boomer technology have since allowed a more detailed picture to be built up of this subaquatic region, but no method of analysis so far developed has proven accurate or sensitive enough to gain a true picture of the surface of this undiscoverable ground. In my own nocturnal explorations through the briny ribbons of the North Sea I discovered hollows within hollows, narrow burrowing passages into the sand and soft clay of the trenches, down to the stiff clay and sand of the seabed; and, within that, those narrow fissures within the depths of the trench which I have already mentioned, and which run far deeper and steeper than any ship may measure; and from which the emanation of fine currents of water could be felt by their temperature differential, tickling as they did at my skin. Had I felt the desire to go further, I would have discovered no doubt a route through all the clay deposits, through the shale, past the igneous anomalies, in whose glacial pebbles the ancient fissures can be traced in varicose patterns, down, through cretaceous chalks and flints, down through the sandstone, through the pools of oil and pockets of gas, down, past fragments of the Manicouagan asteroid – if, indeed, it existed – down through the mudstone, the metamorphic crust which had been Avalonia, and which was now no more, down, down to the igneous origins of us all, where the heat can be felt through the dark rock, down, through the cracks, where the water is already gas, and the sublimating minerals spurt out; down, into the iron and nickel bath, the swirling flood of molten metal, that which, like the crust above, will eventually itself solidify as the earth passes into middle and late age, and like the creatures which live on its surface feel, with the advance of age, the galvanic force within ebb away to open the pathway to the approach of death; down, to that ball of metal so dense of itself that it has solidified in spite of the excesses of its temperature which it itself promulgates, spins, keeps melted all that surrounds it, that which is the same as itself, the ball which spins like a fury in its cage at the very centre of the earth, and whose minor aberrations can be detected in the quivers of needles we place for what reason we cannot say to measure the flux of magnetism. By an ineluctable process, now at the centre of things, there at the core of this spinning ball, and with no more down to be found, I was led back further to a contemplation of the gathering of these initial metals one to another, the beginning of us.

So it was that for a long time I lay upon my side through the night and thought my way into that singular event, the origin, an initial combination of nothing but elemental particles, which, given only time, yielded an entire planet. It was only then that it occurred to me that the formula 'dust to dust', which appears to be so incontrovertibly terminal, does in fact express also beginning, that first gathering of the planets in making of themselves, and that without knowing it, many had said what they did not know but certainly felt: in my beginning is my end, in my end is my beginning. Every little mote, we must admit, declares: I am Alpha and Omega, the beginning and the end, the first and the last. The universe, in its youth, must have been a fearsome thing, and yet how quickly it lost the greater part of its zeal, matured, settled down and waited, now in its vast middle age, for the long drag back in to begin again at the next big bounce, for how else other can it be?

★

The Witch Ground Graben which can be observed in the North Sea, running north-west to south-east between the Moray Firth and Viking Graben, presents a picture of what may happen if one becomes too heavy for the world, if what supports us suddenly is found no longer to be capable of supporting us, and the fault lines open, and we sink. Under the right light, a graben can be seen to have opened up on the surface of the moon, and thus what we had considered to be cold, lifeless, uniform rock, nothing but an accumulation of undifferentiable and homogeneous matter – what, in fact, we in all probability have failed to give proper consideration to at all, except insofar as poetry, that mirror of signs, has turned the moon into – might in fact be as living

as our earth, except that there are and can be no trees, and trees are everything.

There exists a cryptic fragment in the diary of one James Skeltone, a Berger in seventeenth-century Wiltshire, recording an encounter with John Evelyn, one to which I cannot help myself being pulled towards, though I cannot say why: 'Today met and went walking with Evelyn, the King's great advisor on all matters arboreal – a poet of the tree – and he informed me that the centres of trees are in fact dead. I did not know this, I said. Nobody does, said Evelyn. Neither that it is the same with men.'

*

Whenever I seek to approach the matter directly there is a shifting, like the ordinals of the map, where north replaced east as up, and abruptly I am exiled from a vision of the matter, even though that matter be myself. I will try to say all that I can plainly say:

On the evening of Monday 4th May, two men walking a dog in the fields north of Stoke-by-Clare in Suffolk came upon the dead body of my brother. The dog, it must be supposed, had strayed from the path at the edge of the field into Lords Wood, because, so I remember being told, his body was found hanging from a tree deep within those woods, and one of the two men expressed surprise that they had found it at all. I say it was the evening that he was found, but I cannot be certain of this. Perhaps it had been the morning, and the police were preoccupied and did not pass on the information immediately. All I know is that I received a phone call from my father at about half past ten at night, just before the last light of day entirely vanished from the sky. Certainly it was after 10pm, because the first two thoughts I could form out of the vertiginous rush of terror which was blowing all around and through me was that I must have a drink, and I must smoke

34

(though I had given up long ago), and the shop at the end of my road had closed a half hour before.

Of course, it would be possible for me to say when exactly these men had found the body, just as it would be possible for me to discover how they had found themselves walking the fields together, and for what reason they had ventured into the woods, why the dog had led them there, and also when my brother had thrown one end of the bale twine over the bough – so characteristic of him to have cut the string from a bale in the fields for his scheme rather than to have bought it, and I could ascertain the truth of this assumption also – as well as how long it had taken for him to expire, the moment by date and time, near enough, of that expiration; of what species of time it is within which death comes upon a body; how long after that therefore that he had been hanging, after he had become his body, this – it – and in fact all of these events, these truths, not merely possible to be discovered but easy also. All I would need do is to stand, reach up to my left, above the printer, up to the top shelf, pull down the dog-eared white envelope and read the coroner's report contained within it. But this is not something I have been able to bring myself to do.

*

Some nights, as the reader can surely attest, are in fact eternal, and to be cut wakefully adrift in them can be an ecstatic experience if the day is filled with the machinery of suffering. It was on one such night as this, not long after you had gone, that I for some reason alighted upon recalling to myself the story of Jacques Piccard and Don Walsh taking, in January 1960, the petroleum-floated bathyscaphe *Trieste* to the bottom of Challenger Deep, a slot in the bottom of the Mariana Trench nearly 11,000 metres below the surface of the sea – an aberration to the sphericity of the earth of greater magnitude than the highest of its mountains, though hidden. In interviews following this feat, Piccard reported that they had seen, swimming at the meeting point of salt water and the deep layer of diatomaceous ooze gathered in a blanket over the seabed, subjected to pressures equivalent to that of a small automobile pressing down upon the area of the pad of one's thumb, a sole-like flatfish, complete with two eyes, both on its upward-facing side – the one, as with the common soleides, having crept by long compulsion through the generations out of its symmetry to join the other. 'Even as I saw him,' Piccard later wrote, 'his two round eyes on top of his head spied us – a monster of steel – invading his silent realm. Eyes? Why should he have eyes? Merely to see phosphorescence? The floodlight that bathed him was the first real light ever to enter this hadal realm.'

It now seemed incredible to me, thinking about Piccard and Walsh, that these few words could transport the reader, if only for an instant, into occupying the bathyscaphe with these two men below, up out of the depths and across the gulf of time, even of death, for Piccard died a decade before I even encountered the story.

'Slowly, extremely slowly,' he continues, 'this flatfish swam away. Moving along the bottom, partly in the ooze and partly in the water, he disappeared into his night. Slowly too – perhaps everything is slow at the bottom of the sea – Walsh and I shook hands.'

Piccard and Walsh's report was greeted with scepticism at best by the scientific community (more commonly with outright derision) until Piccard felt it necessary to retract his statement, admitting that he was no biologist, and that the sole could in fact have been a sea cucumber, and yet it is the eyes he recalls, and the vividness of the account, Piccard's incredulousness at the presence of eyes in this deep dark, surely means that it must be true. In my times of nightlong waking I sometimes hear a voice, or perhaps speak it. It is not my own, but neither is it entirely another's, and yet I have my suspicions as to who it really is.

—Don't you know, the voice has said, that I along with many of my type was and am down there, now and for all time, and there's a whole lot more than soles and sea cucumbers to be carrying on with. In truth, a host of forgotten deities and superseded mythica still sit down there in the diatoma. Odin has on his silver helmet, Puck a crown of mathematical flowers. Pan licks at his own knees and bleats for fun when the two are confused: Puckleberry Pan! he crows, bleats again, blinks square eyes and performs a goatish spin in the ooze which propels up a fine ladder of phosfluorescent algae in a double helix, modelling God-knows-what species of grief in the structure of its nucleic acid. And if we, then why not soles? There's everything aplenty down in the bottom of the Mariana Trench, I can tell you.

★

One night I was lying in bed in much the same ecstatic insomniac state as that described above when I caught the very ghost of an odour on the verge of my sense: a tang of smoke. I had given up smoking many years before – fitfully, longsufferingly, fraught with lapses and gnashings of teeth – but still the smell, a lovely, almost a nothing, the edge of a smell, like the blade of a knife as, turning, it catches the light in a glint, hardly smelled, more a taste or even a touch, but so very there, more there than anything else for the afflicted addicted, even God – yes, the smell of tobacco still had the power to transform my experience of the world. I was no longer drifting in the hinterland of sleep but every thought, memory, sensation was channelled through this vivid new excitement, as if I were crossing from one continent to another through a long tunnel and could see a pinprick of unmistakable daylight in the far distance, a new and exotic form of life – or was I merely being reborn? There came a cough, foot-tread on the gravel outside my window, a little whispered thought, cogitation. Can one hear a person think? At that moment I would have been certain of its possibility. I turned on to my other side, made to find comfort, and in my imagination I rolled the perfect cigarette, lit it or didn't, crushed it, inhaled, fled from this temptation, flung it from me, and at once was where I had always been, sitting, with a fine drink at my elbow, sinking into the molecular agitation of the nicotine I had and hadn't inhaled: I began to enter sleep once more.

Nicotine, that ever-grinning Mephistopheles.

Only a little afterwards the sound of the little wheel turning, the scratch of the miniature flint, the brief hollow in time as the smoke sits within oneself, and then the breath out. Mutterings, a short and mocking laugh, little more than a snort, contraries. All these sounds transacted at the borders of my consciousness. I must have fallen into deep sleep at some point though, because when I next woke it was to a loud rhythmic sound of crunching, as if bones were being ground down in a mincer a turn at a time, and my bedroom was entirely filled with smoke. Alarmed, I rose and went straight to the window, where behind the blind I looked down to see a figure sitting and moving back and forth in a rocking chair over the gravel – thus the source of the horrible noise – with a long cigarette holder in its mouth, a cigarette mounted and smouldering, and at an appropriate distance from the figure, an ashtray ranged high on a stem of bamboo with little turds of ash being rolled about in its bowl by the light night-time breeze. Not considering, in my state of shock, that I should discover the identity of this mysterious visitor to my garden, I said out of the window, 'You have filled my room with your smoke,' and closed the sash with nervous speed. I must have gone to the window a dozen times in the course of the remaining night – during which

I found it entirely impossible to sleep – but never did I dare to edge the blind to one side in order to see if the figure was still there, sitting in my garden. And yet somehow I knew that the moment the window had banged shut, he had disappeared in a cloud of smoke or mist.

Since this first visitation I have felt the presence of this figure return on a number of occasions. I say *this* figure, but I have no evidence for it. Indeed, every time he returns – he is most certainly a he – he performs different habits and undertakings. Sometimes he sits like any other human and smokes; at others, he is a great compacted ball, I would say a concentrated essence of personhood if it did not sound so preposterous. He spins at a fearsome velocity which, though it performs a magnetic attraction upon me from the window above – I am pulled from my bed and can almost feel myself tipping forward out of the sash, and must place both palms upon the frame to stop myself – does not cause the leaves close by, lit by the security light and the moon, to exhibit even the slightest shiver.

★

It does not take much in the way of travel to discover that, as much as everything is connected, nowhere is there any stability to the meanings which we discover in words. Everything that is, seeks to become something else, or it perishes. It is no different in words, which are hungry for turning. Equally, though, everything which is named, previously was not, and acquired that name from something else. Rivers have mouths; might they then have tongues too, as do shoes? Shoes have soles, which in their intimate way with the ground in walking have bequeathed their name to the fish, though by curious chance that same fish is named from the tongue in many languages (Greek, Arabic, German, Dutch and Spanish). The spines of the fish are named after the thorns of bushes. The haw of hawthorn is the ancient word for hedge, which in turn was named after the act of seizing or catching, which was hunting. What pertained originally only to the hunting of animals could not stay within its enclosure, for words are wily: in turn one could catch sleep, cold or fire – or secure one's door with the same. A hinge is that upon which hangs this thing which swings, but first it was the axis of the earth. 'World' initially denoted a period of time, most commonly that in which one lived, 'the period of a man', for *wer* denoted man, as *werewolf* continues to attest. To wolf is to eat too quickly; and the appetite of humans is prodigious, for they will eat their hats, words and heart out. Time may eat away at the body, just as the atmosphere does the stones of the buildings and the rivers the earth – and just so are we back at the mouthings of rivers. It does seem impossible after all that a river does not have a tongue – how else could the rivers be brought to talk?

★

Did not the Bytham like all rivers seek to obliterate itself even before it was itself obliterated? Is it not true that a river seeks to be not-itself so hungrily that it cuts down through solid rock? So that it might have no more toil and rest in peace as sea? It so wishes to be one with the sea that it will cut an inlet into the hard ground with nothing but water, a substance unsubstantive – hardly there at all – and yet what could there be without water?

When the great fist of ice came and punched you out of yourself, punched even what contained you out of its containment, emptied you, scratched out your existence, then, as it left, filled what remained with the terrible moraine, the refuse of that humiliation, what lap and lick of tongues might we be taught to tell? Did you have a disagreement with gravity over the course and cause of your existence? Did you flow yourself in rebellion upstream? Did you self-flow up in streamyou? Or how might it be, an upflow into truestreamself? Is it possible that the words be made to say? Was it then a punishment for such mischiefs as rivers do sometimes wend? Where now do you stand, twirling your wreathy waters, is it up about the hairy hooves of Pan? Are you so alike in your mischief, the impossibility of your deaths?

It is not normal to ask such questions of a long-extinct river, but it's true that I cannot think of any other way to conduct myself at this time.

*

By virtue of a crook formed by the river Stour, Stoke-by-Clare nestles just inside Suffolk. To look at its representation on a map is to be led to imagine the river having caught the village in its fall from the centre of the county down to its southern extremity, and the burden of it pulling a kink into its course forever. There is little of note to record about the village. There can be found Stoke College, a preparatory school, and guest accommodation provided at Pickwick House. Abutting the gardens of the guest house there is a cemetery, and at its centre stands the church of St John the Baptist, a building built like the hundreds of others in that East Anglian vernacular of flint and brick. To the north of the village is Lords Wood, where he was found. From east to west and back again runs the main road, linking the small towns of Long Melford and Cavendish. Just south of the village, across the Essex border, lies the little village of Ashen, whose name necessarily acquired a resonant quality from the moment that my brother was taken into the Norwich Crematorium in a large box, burned, and brought out in a small one, in which his silt sits, like a genie or sprite of the river.

*

If someone is found, dead, hanging from the bough of a tree by a piece of rope, what do we think about it?

In addition to the twine about his neck, and which had been the cause of death, my brother's body also exhibited two deep chest wounds, one of which punctured a lung, and there was found a belt strapped about his body and arms, presumably placed there as a means of preventing him from seeking to prevent what he intended. The tips of his toes touched the floor but bore no weight. How it comes to be, in spite of all my efforts, that I know so much I cannot say. The coroner's report – that which I must but must not read – asserts (so my mother has informed me) an open verdict. I wonder sometimes how my brother would respond to this final humiliation at behest of the state: a denial of his greatest and final intent.

Is it possible to conceive of a creation, of a coming-into-being out of nothing? And yet what is the logical alternative? Must we conclude that logic is faulty, that it might be the wrong way of thinking about things, that there is a limit to its power of making? In the simple tethering of a belt about the torso and arms is so much of significance; an inversion of the creation, but equally a fizzing sputtering denial of logic, or else an admission of its inescapability, an attempt to unmake, to uncreate into nothing, to do away with the universe, against which must be negotiated the impossible problem of logic which pits one will against another equal one: existence against annihilation, the ineffable desire to sustain even the most miserable life against efforts to be no more. The hand which may reach to tighten the belt will always be capable of reaching to loosen it – given, of course, the time. Did not Kostas Karyotakis attempt without success to drown himself in the Aegean for ten hours, thereby proving that what he wanted was also what he did not? It is touching to observe the little securities a person takes in an attempt to overcome the instinct to life which they know will surge up at the moment of judgement. But 'touching' is laughably not enough.

More than anything my brother loved to sit out of doors, rolling and smoking cigarettes, drinking coffee, and to think through the labyrinths of logic. His complete imperviousness to the development of any amount of body fat he attributed to the fury of his thinking as it ran algorithms, experiments, equations and matrices through the corridors of his mind all day and night in the pursuit of – what, exactly? On a lower bookshelf, away from the coroner's report, I have his copy of *Stability, Instability and Chaos: An Introduction to the Theory of Nonlinear Differential Equations*, a textbook for graduate students by Paul Glendinning, and whose pages for me are as covered with unmeaning as the baroque texts of the sixteenth century were for the illiterate contemporary inhabitants of Stoke-by-Clare.

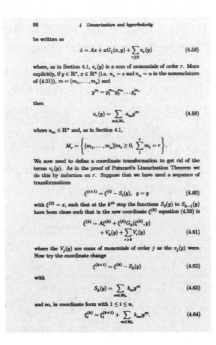

The customary dedication – 'For Fiona,' it says on the first page of the book – is no different, structurally speaking, to that contained in any other book, but I find myself led nevertheless by this book in particular, by the fact of its previous owner being him, you, to a consideration of the mind which formed the thought and feeling for this dedication twenty-five years ago when it was first published, and of what and how the author and Fiona might be doing now. Will you hold me, Fiona, until the morning light? Must everything become asperged with poignancy, I wondered as I closed the book and placed it back on the shelf again.

He followed the type for the mathematical genius so closely that it was impossible not to conceive of it as an act, at least in part. Indeed, one morning – and it really did seem to happen overnight – he was discovered to have acquired an upper received pronunciation, a superior posture, and a quick and straight-legged gait, atop which his head looked down on the things of the world as if they could not be accounted otherwise than disgusting. Part of being himself, whether by act or not, involved a contempt for the common pursuits of people, and especially of material possessions. He owned no house, car, bed, sofa, stereo, records, lamps, chairs, tables, TV, cups, plates, knives, forks, spoons, pans, condiments, spices. He held no birth certificate, National Insurance documentation, payslips, bank statements. His bedclothes were ripped and the duvet perpetually balled up within. He possessed only a few items of clothing (all of them ragged), occasionally a bicycle (until it became by mysterious process stolen or thrust into hock), no more than five or ten books, a guitar (though this was subject to the same perils as the bicycle), and occasionally a phone and laptop (the last of these now standing upright in my cupboard, as if in imitation of a book). On every one of his bedroom floors I ever saw there was a layer of loose rumpled paper, often a foot or more deep, exhibiting fragments of writing, numbers and equations crossed out, and beside the bed a rudimentary spittoon made of no more than a few sheets of this discarded paper placed on top of one another, and which was covered in large globules of brown-green mucus which he had dredged up from his lungs during the night and spat over the edge of the bed. Visiting him in Swansea in 2010 or thereabouts, my dog at the time refused to go up the ladder and into his bedroom in the prettily converted roof because of the smell which poured down from the aperture above – a dog for whom every other noisome stench was the cause of excitement and anticipation. Through self-neglect, people will say, there is already detectable the dreadful coming of death. No, this is just the way he was.

If anyone could have circumvented the logical problem of the belt it was him, and yet I have heard that one arm he had pulled free from within this clasp in order – but no, he ran out of time.

★

From the very beginning I decided I would and could only make a record of the facts, but from the moment that one sits down to write, it becomes clear that any statement, no matter its simplicity, is a poor approach to that many-sided prism, this nexus of intersecting points of view, and that all the light which passed through a single moment or act in time is now scattered, and that truth is forever inaccessible because it never really existed. There was merely a certain structure of significance in evidence at a certain moment in time, waters within what we have decided to call 'ocean' though it be utterly without definite limit or constant matter – though it be only an idea, in other words. The present, and its connection with what precedes and follows it, is, as the scientists say, probabilistic. In a moment of enlightenment which shocks me by the quality of its newness I understand that to make such a record of what happened is to accede to a bureaucratic vision of truth, to the Law contained in and promulgated by the Coroner's Report – there is no truth in such documents, only bloated and gouty facts.

I am thinking here of occurrences in the daily life of any given individual – who can say what mysterious processes underlie the most mundane of actions, the dusting of a shelf, clearing of a drawer or bringing down of a certain book and no other in order to discover what might lie within. But even those verifiable occurrences which, like the planes that cross above us in the high air, we leave as a bureaucratic trail behind us in data and paper are not so simple as one might be led to imagine. Take for instance the legal agreement made between Mark Stanbridge and the state in regard to his mental health: one may find, I remember him telling me, if in possession of the appropriate clearance and an ability to negotiate the archive of Essex Social Services, a signed agreement to the diagnosis 'Schizophrenia'. The signatory, being my younger brother, and thus well known to me, had, since adolescence, refused with a vehemence exhibiting phobic magnitude to visit any healthcare professional. This, he maintained for many years, was because during his last visit to a medical practice, undertaken while under the influence of LSD, the doctor had made inappropriate physical contact, and he was forced by a resultant terror of violation to flee the examining room. Sometimes he had vaulted the desk, sometimes leapt through the open window, and in some versions several of the practice nurses pursued him down the street. I have a similar memory myself of us – me and him – being pursued up the straight gravel path of St Peter ad Vincula church in Coggeshall by two furious pensioners waving sticks who found our presence in the cemetery grotesque, and yet how could such old people requiring such sticks perpetrate such running in our pursuit? Memory versus logic is as to truth vs facts. Many of the things I remember are impossibilities, and yet for me they happened as certainly as that time I threw a stone on an impulse with great arrowing straightness and knew the moment that it left my hand that it would hit you on the side of the head and there could be no explaining why this had happened when it had merely happened, with neither thought nor intention, and you crumpled to the floor.

In a cabinet in an office somewhere, then, is a piece of paper with your signature as its seal which states the impossible, that which you had resisted for years, which could not be so, and so why now? The facts are sometimes, it seems, very far from the truth.

Sometimes when I walk out of the daylight into a church I find after walking around in the gloom for a short while that, coming out into the bright air again, I have a sense of your bicycle being there, leaning against a tree, like you used to lean against trees, smoking of course, a smoking bicycle, now that would be something to see.

*

Sometimes I like not to plummet immediately to the seabed and down between the rocks but rather to come through the air on the wind as a loess, land on the surface of that grey watery mass in the fine form of numerous silt particles, and be carried along the ribbony currents of it all. There are very many of me here, clouding the waters. That is why the sea looks grey.

From the mouths of the rivers which edge the North Sea, enormous quantities of material are transported out into the ocean every day – hundreds of tons from each – though to cup a handful of the water as it passed you would never know. As the fluvial currents mix with the marine – each at its own unique resonant frequency, drag and lift, magnitude of saltation, velocity through three axes, forming a specific Rouse number – the sediment is caused by these conditions to form a representation of them as ripples – straight, sinuous, catenary, linguoid, lunate – and, at the larger scale, as dunes, point bars, braids and deltas. The ripples on a beach after the tide has crept away are like a recording of water, of its particular state of mind at that time and no other.

Down here under the surface of the North Sea the sediments float down like ash and gather into these ordinated forms. Physical processes seem to delight in moving either away from or towards uniformity, though really the delight is ours. The most uniform thing there is, is a sphere because it has only one face, but occupies three dimensions. The most perfect thing there can be, would be that which has no face but occupies all four dimensions, which is perhaps what or where the dead are, whether people or stars. These trenches down here have not been ripped into the crust of the earth by tectonic movement, but merely worn by previous rivers, ghosts, gone. Our own rivers now undertake the long work of filling these channels in, miles wide, hundreds of metres deep. And however many millions of years in the future, it will happen again for these valleys we see around us, then cast beneath the water, from above.

I move Brownianly about down here in the wreathing wriggle of it all. Some of us land on the high plateau of Doggerland and consider that the Thames was once a tributary to the Rhine and flowed round south of us, combining with what would become the Somme, Meuse and Mosel. Some of us float down into the dark trenches in an attempt to make the world round again.

Industrious humans have proven capable of enclosing the soggy masses formed by this underwater drift of dusts, pumping out the water from there and bringing up land of the utmost fertility from the sea. I cannot help but consider that words are the same, actual material forms, used and reused, sent out into the great drifting refuse dump of culture and coming to settle as what we take to be firm meaning, though there is no firmness to any of it. The yawning chasms are still there, below, where the words plummet down to be ground or melted into other forms. I only need to think of him – of you – to know this is true.

In the mornings I emerge from the sea in the bright air of my bedroom and the day feels more like a dream than had my particular existence down there in the water through the long night.

★

It might be useful here to itemise the individual components of the inheritance which I am now in the possession of.

- 1 x Guild GAD-M20NA acoustic guitar, including tweed case (serial number: GAD-48966)
- 1 x Shubb brass capo, with deep patina (why is it that everything you owned was perpetually *filthy*?)
- 1 x Jim Dunlop .60mm nylon plectrum, chewed (why is it that everything you owned contains the mark of your ownership of it?)
- 1 x Hewlett Packard laptop, serial number CND6344508
- 1 x Paul Glendinning, *Stability, Instability and Chaos: An Introduction to the Theory of Nonlinear Differential Equations* (Cambridge: Cambridge University Press, 1994)
- 1 x Morris Kline, *Mathematical Thought from Ancient to Modern Times* (New York and Oxford: Oxford University Press, 1990)
- 1 x ottoman (natural pine, inferior quality)
- 2 x set of bed linen, one featuring sun, moon and stars, the other a geometric pattern

End of list.

★

In the front few pages of the three-volume edition of Morris Kline's *Mathematical Thought from Ancient to Modern Times*, first published in 1972, is the repeated signature of my brother.

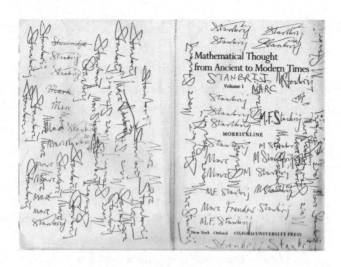

I do not mind admitting that the first time I saw this storm of signatures, when receiving the box which contained the totality of my brother's belongings, I was shocked. (Now, though, I have mastered myself, which is to say killed off pain with the opiate familiarity.) My brother's legal name was Mark Stanbridge, but here he has recorded his name thus only once, and only in a demonstration of its rejection, for it has been crossed it out, a clear statement of intent. (We must interpret the small amount of data which is left to us in order to arrive not at an explanation for *why* but in order to, in order, in, I, —it is unclear why such lists must be made for our dead, which is why they must be made.) Around these crossed-out names have been made nearly two hundred alternative signatures, all asserting the same name in rejection of the old: Marc Stanbrij. Often the first name is repeated alone, often the second, perhaps as a meaningless doodle, perhaps as practice runs for a new existence, an act of wishful thinking – an escape from the inescapable fact of one's provenance always in other people. Strange that the sound of the name should be preserved though, that the name does not definitively sever any connection: not David, John or James, but Marc. On several occasions experiments are made with the inclusion of a middle name, something neither my brother nor I possesses, or possessed. In place of nothing, he inserts 'Freuder' between his fore- and surnames (Freud translating as 'joy, gladness, cheer, pleasure'), and the initials MFS are repeated also, which brought to mind those gravestones upon whose topmost part, often being shaped to accommodate the legend, is engraved: IHS, for Iesu Hominem Salvatore, 'Jesus, saviour of men'. The signatures swarm around the title, the list of contents, the Preface and the dedication, made to Helen Mann Kline – possibly a source for the German middle name, but it seems highly unlikely – mathematics graduate, member of a chapter of Phi Beta Kappa, wife – and editor – of the author, who outlived her husband by nearly a quarter century, resident in Brooklyn for seventy years, mother of three, grandmother to a further three, great-grandmother to four more, ballroom dancer into her hundreds, and acclaimed cook and seamstress. It is so easy to discover the facts of people these days – though what are facts? These two, Helen Mann Kline and my suicide brother – what an entertainment could be had from the observance of their coming together in conversation as they have in writing here on this page, one in a defiant act of self-remaking, the other as the object of an author's devotion.

Elsewhere within the book among the debris of this failed reinvention are the phone numbers of Patch, a boy – now a man – who had played drums in my brother's band (a band named Dennis, after the manufacturer of fire engines, for it was sitting in one such burned-out engine in wasteland in Halstead which gave them the name). Patch, or Patrick, I saw in 1993 or thereabouts eat, for a bet, a large toad which he had kept wrapped in toilet tissue in his school desk for a week, whose guts by the process of putrefaction – it was in springtime, I seem to remember – had turned black and clung to his chin as he chewed. The only other name is Toby, presumably referring to the Toby with whom he had been arrested in the middle of the night while under the influence of LSD, burgling sound equipment from St Benedict's High School. Or was it Philip Morant High School? He was thrown out of, or he left, so many schools. The sound of the alarm, so my brother later told me, was entirely indistinguishable from the general psychic maelstrom which the chemical was causing him to experience. Thus it was a complete surprise to both that they climbed from the window of the school, holding a large keyboard, straight into the arms of members of the Essex Constabulary.

I do remember you practising your signature throughout one summer. You were twelve, perhaps. There was no reason for it, but you practised and practised for hours and days on end. In my memory it lasted a full summer. Pieces of paper covered in the scrawl were strewn through the house, across the floors, being sucked out of the open windows by the hungry wind. Individually a signature is a loose and baggy thing full of its own self only, but to look at a sheet covered in its repetitions, there is a rhythm to it discernible down and across the page. Somewhere in this world there must be at least one of these sheets surviving, covered in the name you later rejected, but they are really not so dissimilar, are they, both expressing a will, a fire of self, a yes world this is me.

*

It was not for a year or more after my brother's death that it occurred to me, quite without weight either of feeling or thought, that a teacher at my old school had killed himself. One Monday, we came into school and were informed that our French classes for the week were cancelled. Within a few hours, who can say where from, the story had circulated that Mr Renfrew had committed suicide. Now, twenty-five or more years later, the only record of this teacher which can be readily found exists in *Vitae Corona Fides: The History of Colchester Royal Grammar School*, in which the commencement of his employment is recorded as occurring in the 1980s, though the unconventional conclusion of this appointment is omitted. Another notable omission is the death, during my time at the school, of Tom Hyde in the year below me, I think, who, being an epileptic, had a seizure and drowned in the school's open-air pool while his classmates and teacher, believing it to be a prank, watched. Neither death is recorded in the book which purports to tell the history of this school, and yet we otherwise find demonstrated a great commitment to recording every detail, perhaps no more evident than in that record of the achievements of Alvin Tracey in 2009 and then Bishamber Jadhav in 2014, who won the National French Spelling Bee trophy, the latter with a very impressive twenty-five words spelled and translated in a single minute. In truth, a person can only be memorialised if that memorialisation does not bring on shame in the memorialiser, and every suicide delivers his or her weight in shame to the family the moment the cord ceases to tremor with the struggle of vanishing life.

*

Perhaps it is only possible to see something, to bear a full account, by looking away. Perhaps the most fidelitous statement cannot be anything but a question. Often I find myself being drawn into hives of information, staring into their workings as if they were agricultural machinery threshing out meaning, or perhaps destroying any possibility of reconstituting it, and in the observation of which I might find myself drawn in bit by bit by the promise of however many absolutes, but to lean in too far is perilous, and in such delvings deep into the creases of meaning one may get caught and obliterated by the ever-turning blades of sense.

*

One morning, after taking the train to Sheringham, I climbed aboard the Coasthopper, an old heavily smoking bus, and began a journey eastwards along the broad arc of the Norfolk coastline, with the impression that I was riding the very tip of one hand of a grand clock. We passed through West Runton, Cromer, Overstrand and Sidestrand, Mundesley and Bacton, until, eventually, I found myself delivered at Happisburgh, where that particular bus terminated. As the bus negotiated its route along the edges of the fields in the final leg of the journey, turning ninety degrees one way and then ninety degrees the other, and so on, I watched the red and white rings of the Happisburgh lighthouse, visible from several miles distant, swing in counterpoint to the motion of the bus, presenting itself first to the left of me, then to the right, and so on, as I sat and watched its approach. It was a happy disorientation to which I abandoned myself on that day, pursuing a creature of the sea across the land, and feeling my progress towards that destination to be subject to alternating currents, currents with their foundations in history, which had by creeping process laid down tenuous borders to the fields a thousand and more years ago by nothing more than human hand and law, only to find these divisions spectacularly endure; while, no more than two hundred metres beyond the lighthouse, the solid ground was being eaten by the sea at the rate of close to three metres each year, a progression which had already eaten up the twin to this lighthouse nearly one hundred and forty years ago.

After alighting, I walked up the shallow incline of the approach to the lighthouse. The freshly ploughed earth on either side of me gave off a distinctive hot fern fragrance which at first gave me pleasure, though soon became cloying. So it was that I was happy to reach my destination. Visitors' hours were presented upon a plastic-wrapped sheet stapled to the door of the lighthouse, the current hour falling within, and yet the door was locked and the building had that air of one which has been closed up for a long time. It was unclear what I should do. I walked around the building and then, as if by the force of some magnetism or gravitational pull, found myself drawn across the field on the other side and soon standing at the clifftop a good three inches taller than my customary height, owing to an agglutination of the heavy clay soil to my bootsoles. Looking out to the grey sea below me, I was caused again to think of the poet Kostas Karyotakis. How, after moving in 1928 to Preveza, a town on the Ambracian Gulf in the north-west of Greece – a town which disgusted the young poet – he was compelled by this disgust to attempt to drown himself in the waters off the enormous eighteen-mile-long Monolithi beach. For ten hours the Greek youth entered and re-entered the sea, but, being an exceptionally good swimmer, discovered himself to be too strong for his desires. Had the Greek come to Happisburgh, he would have found his job easier, for the sandy shores of the Greek coast fell from the soles of his feet readily as dust, while this Norfolk mud I could feel pulling me down already, without – or so I assumed – any desire of death at all. In the end, Karyotakis did succeed in liberating himself from Preveza after only a month's residence by shooting himself through the heart beneath a eucalyptus tree. That morning he had sat in a cafe and contended with himself on the means of escaping this life, drinking over four pints of cherry juice in the process of plucking up the courage to do what needed to be done. Finding by these means his eventual resolve, he left an enormous tip to the waiter and walked across the square and into his oblivion. It is said that the blood from his heart ran down the hill in a torrent and is visible still in a crimson stain on the steps of the Church of Agios Spyridon, though of course blood, following exposure to sunlight – 'the sun, death among all other deaths' wrote Karyotakis – stains black. And so, of the scant thirty-one years of Kostas Karyotakis' existence, there remains only a few short poems and a bright stain of cherry juice.

At that clifftop, looking down at the grey indeterminate mass of the North Sea, and with the circumstances of Karyotakis' suicide first formed in and then drifted away from my thought, I wondered how long I would have to stand in this field of mud waiting for somebody to open the door to the lighthouse, even though it had never occurred to me before that it was a place I had any particular desire to go. Once back at the foot of that building, though, I found the door now ajar, and the dead air which I had felt suffuse the room even from without was now refreshed and even fragrant. The light too now seemed to glance off the things of the room with a renewed vitality, and I was struck by an impression that days if not months had passed while I stood on that clifftop, though in what direction it would be difficult to say.

Entering the lighthouse, I could discover no trace of the human who must have opened the door to allow my entry to the old building. I walked past the desk with its donations box prominently displayed, and ascended the helical staircase until I reached the lantern room, where a large curved and striated lens was seated in a shoe which ran round the circle of the room on a track in an orbit around – and this I found astonishing – just two lightbulbs. One was large and straight-standing, the other smaller and oblique, as if a lesser conjoined twin whose existence was being blotted out by the life desire of its stronger sibling.

At this time I was prone to finding symbolic correspondences in everything, and if this tended towards a feeling of lucidity, it was one which was only later revealed as falsely attributed – in short, a kind of minor delusion. I observed the smallness of the lighthouse bulbs, and the saddle-shaped lens which ran round them like a miniature de-centred universe. I looked out to the vast expanse of the North Sea, and I calculated that this lighthouse too would require demolition or else be swallowed by these advancing waters before another generation had been born and reached maturity.

From the top of the surviving lighthouse, one can look out to where its shorter sibling had been, where now there is only air, spume and light, and if a Mass for that lost brother is brought to mind when one attempts to imagine the vast quantity of candles which once burned in this little domed space, then knowledge of the anachronism – the advent of oil lamps and reflectors displaced the use of candles over eighty years before the demolition of the smaller lighthouse – will never persuade me otherwise.

As I took turns around the lantern room, I could see with ease from above in panorama what can only be faintly sensed if one wanders the roads and paths of the area. In numerous places the long-worn passages of human travel are interrupted by the sea, arrived at too early, a jerk in time. Roads abruptly end, falling away into nothing. The thickness of their tarmac is now visible in profile, a disorienting and in some way scandalous sight, and beneath the road is revealed a medley of earth, pebbles and roots whose wreckage drops down to the beach. Turning and turning about the high building I felt a tidal surge of waters all about me, pushing me first one way, then pulling the other. Unmistakably I sensed a force, a stream of water coiling or uncoiling, reaching into the amorphous saltwater mass like an umbilical cord, moving with the tide, not in and out as with the waters in an estuary, but as if tethered there against its thrashing and moving up and down the body of an unstable and shifting land, one unsure of itself, one fleeing all the time the hard bite of the sea, one immature, unable to steel itself. I remembered an earlier visit to Happisburgh long ago – indeed my first – when one moonlit night I lost my way walking back to my room in the inn and followed road after road into a tangle of lostness until my senses, deprived of light and listening with acuteness to my own tread and the peculiar silence the foliage which grew in the verge made, led me into what felt to be a meditative state in which only a silver aura of road and my spaceless tread on it crossed into my inward self and I was otherwise suspended in time and space. I discovered myself to be only capable of seeing this faint stream of silver road if, against all instinct, I looked away from it. Even this method did not work in places, and the silver aura simply stopped, and I was caused to turn around and trace my steps in perplexity. For many hours I looked for a route back to the inn, and it was only as the sky began to be illuminated that I found my way, confused and exhausted. Later the same day, after a deep sleep, I explored these same roads, wondering where I had been, and what I had experienced; and I was horrified to discover that every one of these tracks abruptly ended and simply dropped off the cliffs into a chaos of smashed tarmac, earth, stones and upended trees and shrubs, and that such would have been my own fate if I had followed my sense of logic – that roads, by their nature, must always lead somewhere – instead of the half-evidence of my oblique vision. Though I suppose oblivion, as much as anything else, can be a destination.

⋆

The cliffs at Happisburgh, formed from three thick glacial deposits and river sediment between, present to the eye of one standing on the beach strata of two million years' depth. Turning, one can look at the waters which had wound across and formed this youthful silty land and which now attacked it from the sea with ferocious force. It is all there, somehow.

It has been said that the ancestor of the Thames had once flowed across the stubby peninsula of East Anglia, joined what has come to be called the Bytham, now long extinct, and flowed out of this north-eastern corner of Norfolk into the North Sea. It is a terrible thing to comprehend the ending of the life of a river, that such a thing can be entirely blotted out of existence, but this is apparently what happened here some four hundred and fifty thousand years ago.

Up by the Bytham's old prehistoric banks – which, if they ever existed (the opinion of the scientists is divided) must still lie remnant under the deposits of time's turning still, no doubt only waiting to be discovered by some instrument or use of light – the houses are demolished before they can fall into the sea, and the residents are moved to other residences at the landward side of the village which are understood to be safe from the destructive advance of the water, for another century perhaps – beyond the common lifespan at least, which is a kind of comfort, I suppose. The area became a site of special scientific interest twenty years past after archaeologists discovered flint tools from approximately 750,000 years ago in the area where the river had entered the sea, which happens to be the earliest recorded evidence of human habitation in Britain. If you walk through the village you may see in the windows of many of the houses a number of worked flints placed there as protection against lightning, a precaution of long and venerable tradition, and one which calls these objects 'thunderstones', believing, as it did and still does in the regional folklore, that they had fallen from the sky and were capable of preserving those who held them close against strikes of the phenomenon which it was supposed created them. Now, the people of Happisburgh do not believe that flint could fall from the sky, nor that lightning be possible of making it, and yet something of the tutelary persists, and where the laws of science leave hollows of knowledge in the mind, the mythic vapour can creep back in and settle into dark shapes, just as the flint-forming silicate did in the subaquatic channels riddling the chalk seabed. As long as there is human mind, there must be myth: only by the production of one is the other procured.

These thunderstones – flints which have been worked by human hand – are of varying antiquity. Some are modern; some appear to be the arrow tips of the Proto-Indo-European tribes of approximately seven or eight thousand years ago; some are very old indeed. One day while walking beside the foot of these cliffs at Happisburgh, the mother of an archaeology student saw a flint lodged down close to the ground which took her interest. She picked it from its place, brushed it off, and noted how a rudimentary cutting edge had been worked into its end. She took it home and gave it to her daughter, who could see what it was: unmistakably a very early Palaeolithic handaxe. The location of its discovery – below the third glacial strata of the cliffs – and the crudeness of its knapping indicate that this flint is much older even than the earliest publicised discoveries of the Happisburgh deposits. This woman, who keeps the flint on a windowsill in her council flat in Norwich, is a friend of mine, and I have seen and held this flint. It is an uncommon experience to hold an object which was made by human hands close to a million years ago – I thought of the familial connection between us, across those fifty thousand generations, while at the same time I reflected on the impossibility of truly thinking it – and the truth that no archaeologist is yet aware of its existence confers to it a peculiar value and grace which would disappear as soon as it was catalogued, theories developed and the archaeological record minutely adjusted in order to account for the data it produced. There is something about the hiddenness of things which confers greater value, how it sits there, beneath the folds of a curtain, unknown, unseen even by the person living there, because it is just another object in an everyday life.

 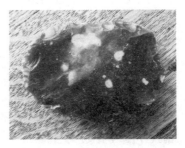

I must have been submerged in these currents of thought within the lantern room of the lighthouse for some time, because it was only when I was brought to a consciousness of my physical surroundings by being asked to leave – they were closing for the day – that I noticed the field I had walked across, like the sea beyond the cliff, was plunged into darkness. I apologised, and as I began my descent from the lantern room, happening to look up to a view of the mollusc-like structure of the tapered stairwell, I was put in mind of what they say of the universe, that it curves in on itself like a saddle. I felt a surge of emotion or significance of some nebulous kind for a correspondence between the insides of this solitary lighthouse – the brother which remained – and something fundamental to my being. I pondered the continuance of its upkeep against all practical purpose, the lighting of its light in the shipless night; and it was not an image of what I had seen which accompanied me for the bus journey back to the city, but rather what I had not: two thousand candles lit in a mass of remembrance for a million years of human time and these few souls sitting on an antiquated thrumming bus at the sharp edge of it all. And if we were drawing in towards the end of human time, then so be it, because there is wonder enough in the fact of being without the franticulations of man to give it necessity.

★

Some rivers seem simply to sicken of the air and green, and to burrow down to make subterranean spaces, caves, stacks, blow-holes, and seek the sea in hidden ways, and who is to say that that is not the way it is with us too? What is it that propels the spinning ball at the centre of us? The great spinning ball of iron at the centre of it all? Is it that everything seeks to reach the centre of itself, though each centre refers thence to another greater centre, and that desire is inextricably linked to rotation, and rotation to the gravitational force of others? It is shocking to learn of the dwarf star PSR J1748-2446ad, how it revolves upon its axis seven hundred and sixteen times every second, that any given point on its equator moves at a quarter of the speed of light. If I close my eyes it is not that I see this pulsar at its ferocious activity, but I feel it, and it makes perfect sense: the intergalactic sublime.

(Sometimes his voice comes through like an untraceable leak of water, still a subterranean river, in words like these:)

It is – it was – myself. I had this ferocious desire which quickened every thought that moved within me. My desire was strong and natural, my pulse was the pulse of electromagnetism. Instruments could detect me by the emission of my many energies in waves. I was a lighthouse for the darkness. I was the most rapidly spinning star. A star which spins at a velocity exceeding certain limits set by its own mass will by certain intransigent physical laws disintegrate – there is no getting away from the limits of physics, we are told – and yet in what contempt do

I hold the law! (Yes, I signed my name to a condition of mind, but what is name, law, mind, when there are most rapidly spinning stars?) I pursued the limits set by the speed of light with a hammer in one hand and a bag in the other, a swarm of formulae playing upon my vision. I decided at some formative age to break out of the kernel of time – a grave announcement I believe I made of this onerous act to the cat: I am going to make a time machine – and so I did, so did I. A black hole, as anyone unconstrained by the worship of the laws of light will agree, is a massive star which, passing certain physical limits, has broken the matter of itself out of its own containment in the space-wasting atomic shells, has shrunk every portion of itself into a spaceless space, and now occupies nowhere, content to spin at a speed far in excess of the speed of light, because it has swallowed all the old laws in an attempt to move infinitely fast, in an infinitely small space, in absolute efficiency, until, achieving it, it becomes there/not-there, which is ideal. We come roaring down the birth canal into the light and spend a lifetime attempting to cultivate a calmness at our centres, but the ball of iron keeps spinning, the light keeps being eaten up, and we cannot, too much, and in the end, when we roar back into the darkness, into that realm of desire where our spinning can spin unconstrained, it is filled with fear that we go. But there is nothing to fear. I am a lighthouse for the darkness.

*

Sometimes there is a current to existence that – the body adopting its rhythms and resonances – smudges the edges of the self, to the end that the body and what it does in the world feels to be as natural as the stoop of a falcon or the arc of a stream from a precipice down into the black pool below. When I sit down, you speak. And so that is or must be how.

Yes, sometimes I would find myself moved to write in his voice, which was not at all his, though neither entirely mine, and in spite of this he would be here again.

—Being, at its most fundamental level, comprises a network of switches. The three classes of science as it is now taught in the schools – Biology, Chemistry and Physics – are three ways of looking at the switches of being. They are like those card-rimmed glasses with coloured lenses you used to be handed in the dark way down to the cinema screen: blue, red and yellow. Putting on the glasses makes one set of switches visible, while putting on another pair of glasses enables you to see another set, ones performing other kinds of work, and so on. Even such performances as can be simply stated in language – the catalysis of chymotrypsin, to take an example that immediately springs to mind – are far too complex in their internesting of switches to be comprehended as such. To enumerate and fully account for the work which all the elemental switches undertake in this reaction would occupy all the remaining pages of this book. If we think rather than observe, though, we can discover that everything which is, is built up of the simplest of switches, just as a cathedral is made of stones. We must think our way down to those individual stones – to the mason sitting there on his or her stool and working the planar. We will soon find that nothing which exists is exempted: everything is switches. The difficulty is working down to this unitary level, where the switches act in simple rather than complex states. Simple soil, for example, is a complex of many millions of switching functions, but it is still only that. The work for each of these many millions goes thus: IF such-and-such, THEN such-and-such. If this is not an accurate account of what is occurring, then the activity or reaction or state being studied is made up of more than one function and we must divide it into the multiple switching functions of which it is made. In other words, we have not gone far enough down. These switching functions are indifferent to the inorganic/organic division of being – all are at their origin the same function, for otherwise the one could never have sprung out of the other. As to the air, nitrogen's fundamental switch command is IF nitrogen THEN: yes, and thus dinitrogen (N_2) is the most abundant gas in the earth's atmosphere. As to carbon dioxide (CO_2), carbon's switch command is: IF oxygen, THEN: yes (two please). The same is true of every element, compound, individual molecule, solution, suspension, reaction, and so on: IF such-and-such, THEN such-and-such. It is simple: attraction or indifference. The whole of existence is predicated on desire. Up through all these internested switchings being is brought to function until we have voles, comets, fire and leaves of grass. The network grows, the switches embed one within another, the process develops great chains of internested switchings, until a human mind can read a menu and order *moules frites* and a glass of beer. Just because a person doesn't experience the workings of the switches doesn't mean they are not at work within him or her. (It need hardly be said that such switching is most clearly seen in the work of DNA in encoding the cellular manifestation of the individual, whether that individual be a larch, beaver or CEO.) Now, when the body dies, the tissue, flesh, fat, bone, fluid, and so on which had constituted and enabled the performance of the mind's switchings within the organ of the brain deteriorate – in accordance with every manner of impossibly complex internesting of impossibly simple fundamental switching involved in the act of decomposition, of course – until the individual components which had enabled the functioning of the mind are scattered, whether by burial or burning, into the air, ground and sea. Now, these elements are no less involved in switchings than they were when housed in six-inch proximity to one another inside the skull of a human being, a proximity which, under the auspices of a grotesque act of chance, allowed this network to function for a brief spell of time.

(I heard recently that the human mind is the second most complex system in the universe. The first is the universe.) To take an example, the manganese which had undertaken crucial activities in the disposal of harmful ammonia in the body, switching water ON as a nucleophile in the attack of L-arginine (hydrolysing it to ornithine and urea), is now down in the ground, and is so turned ON by iron, its switches locked in terminal attraction, that it cannot be found as a free element in nature. Although the human brain which had once been the locus for the gathering-together of these elements is no longer existent, the operations performed by the elements of that human mind are no more or less complex or numerous now that they are dispersed throughout an area which at first is small – limited initially to the interior of the oven; then, as the smoke rises, into its flue; further, out of the opening of that chimney into the local atmosphere above the crematorium, yew trees and serried gravestones; and then out to cover perhaps the extent of a county, depending on the velocity and direction of the wind – though eventually the hinterland will expand to cover the entire earth, and in fact, after the destruction of the earth by the sun, will move beyond.

What had begun as a doodled voice would become a hectoring treatise, one I would sometimes interrogate as if real and external to myself.

Does this mean then that your mind is out there doing its mad work still? Your switches all ticking back and forth this way and that, but out there in the soil, on the sea, and up there in the sky in pure elemental force?

Yes, that is exactly what I mean. Infinite is my new kingdom.

Then how is it that you are come to speak to me now in this voice? I found myself led to enquire, but the answer was unsatisfactory:

Ah, this voice is not me at all, but your guilt.

66

*

I say that this is your voice, but what this voice is, is not you, nor yet me. Is it perhaps more the air or trees, the horses and cavernous holes in the earth, a world-voice, I cannot say.

Sometimes the voice is angry, sometimes competitive. Sometimes it is honest, setting things straight, as to its view of the matter. Often it brags of its exploits, achievements, the greatness of itself. 'Many are the mischiefs of the voice' – which is why I think of you. It references multiple and varied sources, commits outrageous transgression of publicly acceptable discourse. Several times already today it has proclaimed itself a Puck:

(1) Monday morning, 3am

The world-orderers, feeling threat where threat is, rail against all Puckishness, forgetting that mischief is the very heart, centre and sun of life. The very notion of organicity entails the turning of one thing into something else – of everything which is one, into many – otherwise, how? If the mischievousness of being is so, then am I not the most mischief of all? I turned myself back into raw matter for the next round, my own big bounce. I welcome myself into myself, across death, and now I am everywhere as elemental pawls and switches, waiting. So stop that now, and rejoice.

(2) Some time shortly after lunch

Note well: the Puckishness of dust, the Oberonishness of planets. In my beginning is my end, and both are at once the same. There is always time. The big bounce is start and finish, and I see you start in a shock of terror, which is why the word is the way it is, two-headed, brimful of Janusishness. Did you not know that? How else might the dust be made to live again, to fly, to form stars which thence may synthesise all the elements in their happy cores? Extraordinary developments require concentrated heat and out-of-the-way-ness, hydrothermal vents, the dark hearts of stars. Out here in the everywhere you can't see me and the work I have come to do, my many elemental switches, pangalactic ticklings with my yellowbrowned fingernails, curved like a bunting's beak, full of mischief. When I smoke, which is always, I breathe the whole universe in, mix it like I were a cup and spoon and it the milk in tea, and it comes all jumbled up and ready to begin again in all its diffuseness.

(3) Just before midnight

The folding of protein: me. The migration of rivers: me. The flight of horses: me.

I am all that is obverse, inverse, converse – perverse, in fact. I am verse itself, potatoetaster, riddlebanger, lovelorner.

★

A myth starts as a little nut or seed – myths are most like trees, you see – holding within a power of doubling and more the world. It is a growing of multitudes out of one, it divides, but is more. Myth grows, is green, shoots up in its manybranched strivings, to reach what it moves toward, until, at maturity, it ceases, makes what it had sought to find, and settles into its old ways, like an old man sitting, grows hollow at its dead centre very like an old man sitting, falls into decrepitude, and dies. From thence it is good only for fuel, burned once, burned twice, and then it is spent.

If I make memorial for one, I make for all, across all time. He for whom the signs were too significant; we for whom they have been emptied, or are weighed down with dead weight of the deceased.

*

I wonder if, walking over it, one senses the newness of this land. The fine silts, loesses and moraine of Norfolk – we are living on debris, a refuse dump, but one which is hungry to sprout new life; fecund and promiscuous. The sea eats into the cliffs of Happisburgh like a machine, which I suppose is what it is: one component in a vast recycling plant. Everything turns in circles, cycles, wanting to become other – always in the midst of this unstoppable spinning, separation, tearing, collision; foldings and upliftings – like the words for things want to leap across meaning and illuminate some other department of being with an originality which gladdens.

But what if that leap is pernicious? Such a pleasure it is to receive coded messages, but not for the sender if they are unsent.

Sometimes the voices I hear – not hear, but intone, without sound – sometimes the voices are brisk like water under the light. Not so long ago the land mass which has come to be called England lay over the oblate of the earth, prostrate under the equatorial sun. Not so long ago the Anglian ice sheets pushed fists across the same conglomerate of rock and earth, and when the ice melted had obliterated everything. Buried under your feet as you walk is a river channel which had no name, a subterranean waterghost, a lost source. Bytham they call you. Without you, where can all the water go? Are you twin to Ruoshui the weak river, that within which no thing can float? A feather landing upon its surface finds no uplifting but is dragged down into its untenable depths. None can swim in it, neither in you, unfindable unwater, choked with moraine, river of dust and spent time.

★

I spend hours, days, weeks trying to uncover the final word on the river Bytham. Did it exist? Where did it rise? What was its course? Where did it end? How was it obliterated from the face of the earth? It is astonishing to think that a river of hundreds of miles in length can be entirely erased from existence. These things grip me with such strength that I cannot even comprehend that they do this because they have become you – that everything, at the moment, is you.

Is it that you were too thirsty for the world and what lay beneath its crust? Did you dive down? Is that where you are still, deep in riverthought, waterlogic, making for the sea subterraneanly, ever closer to the spinning ball of iron and zinc?

Rivers have long been supposed the images of life, and the sea one of death, where the river terminates, but everything is upended and inverted, the dead rivers speak to each other through the long nights and the sea is yet to be born. Whether or not the Bytham ever existed, whether or not the Thames flowed with it up into the north, a narrow dividing line now swallowed by the North Sea, up through Doggerland, I hear them converse with each other. Rivers have spoken in many of the world's myths, and language – speech specifically – is likened to a stream. But never did I feel the necessity of preparing for the springing of these two, until now.

Perhaps it is a condition of the Bytham that it remains unread, unknown, until a chance uncovering. I read recently of the footprints of a family of five, of five pairs of feet discovered in Happisburgh mud. They had been held beneath the sand and stones for half a million years until a storm swept up the coast and, scooping up this debris, revealed them. I considered how these kinds of revelations of the distant past must be happening all around us all the time, but only a minuscule proportion of them is detected. There is something glorious about it. On the contrary, it confers a peculiar feeling, close to pain, to consider that two weeks after they were revealed, and after such long long waiting, the sea had washed all traces of these five people into oblivion.

Do they speak truth, now, to say that you never were? Did no river flow for your waters? Were you only ever an idea? Or were you two, as some say? Or more?

It seems for the time being that everything is possessable by this lost person, and to resist is futile, ever aggravating matters.

It seems for the time being that everything must orbit this person who is gone, whether the voice speak ill or good.

It seems – but what is seems, except only everything.

*

It is in the evening of the day that I find myself to be most susceptible to remembrance, and an attendant melancholy sweeps into me like a dusty gust of wind through an opened door. It is too the most beautiful moment of the day, its end, suffused with peace and quiet and an afterglow of the day's light. It may well be that it stands symbolically as a moment of reckoning at the death of each day; or perhaps it is just a quirk in my nature, like a knot in a tree trunk, an imperfection that is an indispensable and inevitable characteristic of oneself. In any case, it was at this time of the day that I found myself walking back from the lighthouse toward the village where I was hoping to discover that the buses were still running, when I passed an overgrown path leading up to the door of an old derelict house, the sight of which shocked me with its familiarity, and yet it was a familiarity – just as one often finds in the flash of a stranger's face – which I struggled to locate in experience. It was only an hour or so later, sitting in the stifling diesel-scented plumes of heat on my bus (I will call it mine, because I was alone, and this is how it seemed, striking me even as driverless for some long moments, a mesmeric journey) that I realised the house had reminded me of a time from long ago, when, living within the dilapidated walls of an old house very similar to the one I had just seen in Happisburgh, I learned of Christian Friedrich Garmann.

One winter's day I received a call from a friend whose cousin or nephew – or perhaps friend, I cannot remember which – needed help clearing a house she had recently acquired at auction. Being at the time between jobs, I packed a small bag, walked to the station and took a train along those tracks which travelled like a belt across the narrow waist of the country until I was where I was required to be. The weather was filthy, the days impossibly short – that interval between the nights seemed only ever to become half day, and then for a mere few hours, as if the light was anaesthetised and couldn't summon sufficient interest in the world to explore it. The house, when finally I came to the overgrown lawn which obscured its path and stood before it, was, even from this vantage point and with my limited knowledge, obviously beyond any economical salvation. Its timber frame sagged, great scabs of brick and mortarwork were eaten away as if by monstrous insects, every iron gutter was hanging in dishevelment, tufted with shrubbery – there was even a small tree growing high up at one corner – and, most terribly, the chimney stack had fallen through the centre of the house and left a gaping absence which one could feel as some emanation or ghost all the way to the plot's boundary where the iron fence was steadily turning back into ore. I entered the place, settled into the least ravaged room, and reflected on the folly of the new owner. At that very instance, I discovered myself to have developed an extreme aversion to this person which had no need of our ever having met for its germi- nation. In the course of several weeks' habitation in this place, I achieved virtually nothing in the task of clearing the contents in preparation for the builders to enter and begin the pursuit of what must be a galvanic miracle if it was to restore the place to life. There was no beginning to the task, because there could be no end. So, for several weeks I walked from room to room and picked through what had been left by the previous owner – who, presumably, had died some time ago of old age – and reflected on what had been added by nature. The wallpaper throughout was blotted with spores and sagged out from the sodden plaster beneath. Spiders had woven web upon web up along the alcoves, and each had eventually collapsed onto those beneath it to the effect that the whole room appeared to have been stage-dressed in the fullness of all nature, complete with these cirrus clouds in the room's highest stratosphere, a genus of cloud, I recalled, which, according to the specific shape it sometimes took, possessed the name 'mares' tails'. Within the sink trap I discovered a nest of desiccated mice, each resident curled up in permanent sleep. They had presumably discovered themselves trapped there when the drain flooded long ago, and had made the decision to return to their beds to wait. In one room I discovered a portrait hanging below a hole in the roof where the gutter had cracked. The action of the rainwater flowing over the surface of the wall and then the painting itself, had, by a combination of the gradual removal of paint by that infinitesimal work at which water is such an adept and the equally gradual accretion of mineral deposits presumably taken from the matter of the tiles, gutter and plaster above to its surface, entirely erased the face of the sitter from the canvas; an erasure much like one finds from the matter at the centres of gravestones in cemeteries, though the stem of the individual's neck remained visible, leading to and supporting nothing, as did a large part of the background, within which one could observe a large leafless tree whose boughs seemed to be screaming, and below them a rider sitting upon the curiously unanatomical rendition of a horse.

In the room I had chosen for my own were several bookcases stacked with loose papers and portfolios, and upon whose contents were scribbled copious notes. Instead of dragging all the rotten filth out of the house, I sat in my bed with a camping stove and gas lamp on a chair beside me, brewed coffee and stewed noodles from my supine position, and read through all these notes with an alacrity whose pathological tendency I was incapable at the time of perceiving. It is only recently that I have begun to notice certain patterns in the behaviours of my past self; one of these being a compulsion to read, among all the printed material with which we are bombarded every day from all quarters, any and every handwritten note which my eye alights upon. I clearly remember going back to a friend's house after school one day and, standing in the kitchen while his mother talked to us, ignoring her entirely so that I could read a note pinned to the corkboard which a friend had sent in order to thank her for some kindness or other. In short, I was addicted to discovering – or perhaps more accurately, to intercepting – a real human voice, no matter how banal. But to return to the papers I discovered in the old house, there was no overall design to these writings, or none I could detect, only a series of eddies and whirls, subjects taken up and abandoned, or developed into abstraction, or else worked by the author towards a manner of climax, though one which never came, nothing in evidence but a blank for the remainder of the page, with not even a full stop to steady the mind.

One subject among these writings in particular took my interest, an account of the later life and death of the Lutheran physician Christian Friedrich Garmann, whose *De miraculis mortuorum*, first published in 1670, had the dual distinction of being placed on the Vatican's forbidden book index and ridiculed by the early empiricists of the time. As the title suggests, in this work Garmann explores in depth – the book runs to in excess of a thousand pages – the nature of death. What is it? When does it begin? Is this at the same time as life ends, or is there, so to speak, a period of handover, a negotiation between the two? He assembles a panoply of observations on death and its dead – from folk beliefs to verifiable accounts of specific phenomena – and seeks to interpret and assess for the reader's edification, though often he cannot decide. For Garmann, as presumably for his contemporaries, death is complex. It does not form an absolute and perfect abutment with life, like one piece of timber mortise and tenoned to another. Even in death, we may remain, in some way and in some measure, within or at least attached to life. Thus, so the reasoning of his age purported, does the body move even after the heart has stopped. Nails and hair continue to grow. The penis may become engorged and stand up from the body, a common observation among the hanged. In one particularly entertaining part of the book, the story is recounted of a widower who tipped his wife's gravediggers in advance in good will that they carry her coffin with the greatest of care so that she would not be hurt by the jolting. Cases abound, Garmann wrote, of cadavers which squealed like pigs from their coffined places beneath the ground. Among these people, for whom death was not so distinctly divorced from life, there was held a great dread of premature burial, a not unknown phenomenon. So it was that a number of bodies, upon being exhumed under the direction of family members seeking to reassure themselves that their kin had been properly deceased when they entered the earth, were found to have eaten their shrouds or clothing, or even in some cases their own arms.

The handwritten notes to and reflections on *De miraculis mortuorum* ran, so I discovered, to well in excess of the thousand pages which the original work occupied. As I read, I conceived of each individual life as a kind of basin which overflowed continually, which flooded beyond the notions of its antecedents, and which would be flooded by its descendants, and the silt build up into, what? All the remains which we bring to bear in the world. Further to these notes on his investigation into curiosities of the dead, a whole ream of paper – or so it appeared by its thickness – was dedicated to a biographical study of Garmann gleaned from sources which either I could not identify, or, if I could, from texts whose originals I have never been able to locate. It seems that, good empiricist that he was – or that he half-was – Garmann arranged to have himself buried alive in the Trinitatis cemetery in Dresden as a means of investigating the capabilities of the soil of that place, which was so notorious for its flesh-consuming properties that testators demanded that, if they could not be buried there, at least a handful of this miraculous soil be placed in their coffin with them. (Garmann recounts a story of the gravedigger there being compelled to move bodies which had been in the ground a scant nine days, and discovering that every ounce of flesh and viscera was gone, and only a good clean skeleton remained – this, it appeared, was how the people of Dresden in the late seventeenth century desired things to be.) In his experiment, which of course was not and could not have been known to the authorities, either civil or ecclesiastical, Garmann was taken in the night to his resting place – a grave dug for a soldier killed in fighting at Mohács, whose body could not travel as fast as the letter which had notified his family of his glorious demise – was placed in a coffin, and, as is the custom, lowered into the hole he and his associates had appropriated for him, and thereafter covered up with the purportedly hungry earth which had been removed from there. The ingenious physician had fitted a pipe into the top of his coffin, which would pass through the soil above and allow him both to communicate with those above and to breathe. To the steady rhythm of Garmann's voice intoning '*gut*' and '*klar*', his assistants went about the nervous midnight work of piling the earth on top of his box, which intoned a low, hollow B-flat with each clod drop, until, as near as finished, hearing a sound and seeing the light of a lantern, they fled. Sheltering in the stable of a nearby tavern for the night, at first light this band of men climbed again over the cemetery wall and plodded over sod and great weavings of roots, through damp leaves and low-lying mist, but in no way, despite the freshness of the earth above him, could they discover where they had buried the venerable physician. For days after this terrible night the men tramped through the cemetery, though their numbers declined one by one until only a single man was left, though even he ceased soon to come, and the doctor was given up entirely. It was only when the soldier's body had finally been returned to his native soil that the grave which had been dug for him was required to be claimed. The authorities, of course, unlike the physician's associates, had all the necessary records for the rediscovery of a grave which as far as they could recall had already been dug. It was a mystery. The gravediggers – there were several, for Trinitatis was and still is a large cemetery, and requires now as much as it did then constant vigilance for the disposal of Dresden's dead – were questioned, and one indeed remembered distinctly digging this man's grave, for the earth was not homogeneous or undifferentiable by locale, but held as it were a manner of narrative through its many layers, and this story he could certainly remember well, for it was a good one. He took the authorities to the plot they had identified, and witnessed with his own eyes the filled-in grave and, looking curiously, noticed the protrusion of the little pipe through which Garmann had breathed and also intended to converse, and around which the gravedigger had then carefully to dig. When, finally, they pulled the physician from the ground – nine days it had been, living off the condensation which gathered in the bore of his pipe – he blinked heavily, thanked those by whom it had been the Lord's

77

pleasure to discover him, and scuttled away before investigations into differentials, Lord-to-Lord – his vs theirs – could be commenced. He visited each of his friends in turn in order to let them know that he was alive, but within the first few visits became aware that these individuals, in spite of appearances to the contrary, believed him to have perished in the ground, and that his spirit had now returned to haunt them for either their lukewarmness as friends or incompetence as associates. He laughed, cajoled, and in the end persuaded them of the truth, which was that, contrary to what one might imagine, it was really a magnificent thing to be dead. The body slid away, as did the time – all the ratchets, springs, coils, cams, dials, and so on, of human life – until there was felt only an absence of pressure, almost barometric, as the bounds of self were breached, and by such a process all bounds revealed for what they were: a fabrication.

It was only later that Garmann discovered – or so the notes I read seemed to imply, for they were disordered and tentative in statement – that, aside from this temporary sense of lightness which he thenceforth felt, there was one peculiar and permanent outcome of having been buried alive within the flesh-eating earth of Dresden's Trinitatis cemetery, which was that he was forevermore entirely unable to prevent a surge of fear engulfing him whenever he heard the word *riesig*, which is to say in English 'massive'.

★

Now, sitting on the bus as it traced a zigzag path beside the straight line of the coast like a meandering river which refused to comport to the laws which govern water and drain into the sea, I found myself stuck inside a maze of significance in regard to this long-forgotten recollection of Garmann's logophobia. It was impossible for me to discover even the reason of the story's significance to me, let alone the reason for Garmann's reaction to the

78

word. Perhaps it was the discrepancy of scale opened up between what a word is – nothing really but a lost sound – and what we attempt to make it mean. And yet the very effect of this inadequacy of the word is the cause – at least in this particular case – of its adequacy, because true massiveness is terrible and should rightly be feared, if not most of all, then at least beyond the bounds of what can be reasonably controlled. And so in turn we are deeper in the maze, translocated to another plane of its convolvement, deep within a within, chamber upon chamber, and stuck there with only fearful words, which in truth constitute all that is the world and every of its meanings, turning a blizzard of limitless meaning around us. And I did not wonder for a minute that seeking to escape from this chaos of signification, one without stability or bedrock, by recourse to a cord and the bough of a tree would be a very justifiable temptation if one had become marooned there.

★

There follows a list of unwritten stories about my brother:—

i.   The Nose, part I: When in the course of a single Saturday night in the barrack town of Colchester he did sustain attacks by five (5) separate groups of men, one though not necessarily the last resulting in a break to his nose affecting by some 15 or 20 degrees the perpendicularity of that organ relative to the face;

ii. The Nose, part II: When, several months later, another group of men attacked him in the same town, breaking his nose back into place more perfectly than any surgeon could have dreamed;

iii. The Burger Wager: Being an account of a wager made between himself and a friend named Patrick (the previously met 'Patch'), in which the originator (Mark Stanbridge, known to himself as Marc Freuder Stanbrij) of the bet must, in a single sitting, eat fifteen (15) Big Macs; whomsoever wins the bet forfeits the pleasure of paying for the burgers (the result being 12 down, and a public sickness);

iv.   The Sorrowful Tale of the Crowbar: In which the protagonist 'borrows' his mother's last ten pounds, buys a five (5) foot crowbar, and prises the fronts from the phone boxes of Colchester, yielding in just a few hours a profit of infinite magnitude (one of a little over five orders of magnitude had he paid for the tool himself);

v.   The Burning of the Historic Fruit Tree: (The less said about this the better.);

vi.   The Breaking of Muhammed's Leg: The disputed account of how a tackle undertaken pursuant to the art of football resulted in a fractured tibia;

vii. You Are Lost/I Am Not Lost: Being the touching account of how a small child became lost without knowing it, and was found, several hours later, a mile and more away, at the unfrequented end of a long beach, immersed in the serious task of collecting feathers;

viii. The Lost Fortnight: In which the teenage protagonist, having the house to himself for two weeks, spends the £200 given to him for food on amphetamines, marijuana and LSD, and has a lovely time;

ix.   The Gravedigger: In this story, two brothers and a cousin discover in the churchyard at the back of their house a cracked gravestone – one of the ones which extends like the lid of a tomb over the full length of the coffin – and attempt to break through to view the corpse they erroneously believe lies just underneath;

x.   The Womb: Benumbed by the powerful effects of hashish, the hero of this story asks a friend of a friend if it would be okay for him to 'crawl up into your womb'. The request is declined.

xi. The Delusion: Where one monkey, two rabbits, etc., etc., are found to mean all that they can mean, and the downward spiral begins, unto this end:

xii. The End: In which the protagonist flees into the woods for nine days and nights, and as conclusion hangs himself from the neck until he is dead.

*

Memory, they say, is just like any other of the faculties and requires exercise in order to flourish. And yet, what if one wants to sink into indolence, into a fog of no-past? When we shut our eyes against some fear or other, the sight may disappear, but the fear redoubles, and so we open our eyes again, not in order to face our fear, as the moralists will have us bravely do, but because we are in truth more cowardly even than we thought.

In one of my earliest memories I am sitting in the cemetery of St Peter ad Vincula in Coggeshall with a friend whose name is now lost to me, and we are thinking about a particular girl. The thinking must be transacted at this particular place, between these particular graves, on this particular patch of daisy-speckled grass and no other. Perhaps it was a necessity then to be free of the familiar domestic surroundings of the home in order to think fully, in earnest, with every mechanism of the will fixed upon this girl, the appearance of whose face, no less than the letters of her surname, has also slipped from my memory. I do know that her name was Sarah, and that I could have been no more than six years old, but I was so deeply in love that thinking now nearly forty years later about that patch of lawn between the graves, am I not there again, entirely, filled with devotion? Our garden, with our neighbours', backed onto a little muddy path kept dark by a thick laurel hedge, and which formed, on its other side, the boundary of the cemetery. All we needed to do was walk a little along the path and push, at the low child-shaped hole, through the frieze of oval shadows made by the silhouetted leaves, and there we were, in the bright day beyond, the broad open space of the burial ground. Every grave was individually different, though there were family resemblances: crosses, rectangular headstones, arched headstones. Some were stones laid out as quasi-tombs, though being hardly above ground level they were too low to house a coffin outside of the earth, something we children did not apprehend. The casement of one of these graves had broken, and we spent an afternoon attempting to lift the stone using a spade for a lever so as to get a glimpse of the body beneath. I remember these low tomb-style graves being covered with a synthetic translucent stone of either green or blue. To me, these stones were highly mysterious, perhaps because of their proximity to death as much as because of their colour and appearance, and I took several handfuls of them which I kept in my pockets for weeks, not knowing where to keep them or how to dispose of them without incriminating myself.

Wherever I lived as a child I heard the church bells ring out the major scale from the octave down to the tonic, and as the ringers proceeded, expertly or inexpertly (I could not say even now), the diatonic intervals drifted through time until what had been a steady downward progression was scattered into a bespeckled sonority which seemed perfectly to reflect the work of my consciousness, and the work of the cemetery beyond the laurel hedge, both of which shattered and scattered the daytime conception of the straightward arrowing train of time, calling it out for what it was: just one way of organising experience. Invariably I heard these bells, and the strict pattern to the language of the wood pigeons, from my bed, in the process either of waking or falling asleep, and the sounds would smear into the mirrorworld of my dreams. My brother's childhood room lay down the other end of the corridor, and never once until now did I imagine what passed through his thinking and feeling under the pressures of the same experience. We are more similar than you think, he said to me once. Yes, but how much more, if I already think it? And what does this mean as regards what awaits me, in the fog of the future?

★

Recalling Garmann's entrapment beneath the ground and his consequent fear of the word *riesig*, I had cause to recall also the moment I heard the story of Rom Houben, a Belgian, who dwelt and indeed continues to dwell in a kind of cave, though in this case within himself, in Liège. It was November 2009, and I was standing on a gallery above the concourse of Berlin Tegel waiting for my gate to be called. Although it was winter, I distinctly remember the bright sunlight which punched through the series of high windows running the length of the hall and filled the whole airport with an almost intolerable whiteness. I picked up a copy of *Der Spiegel* from one of the many racks and, after discarding the main paper – I have never been able to tolerate the news – I flicked through the supplement until my attention was drawn to an article about the Belgian man in question. I folded the magazine around on itself and, shading my eyes with one hand, began with my intermediate German to puzzle through. I read how Mr Houben, who had been diagnosed as being in a persistent vegetative state since a near-fatal car crash twenty-three years earlier, had recently had his diagnosis overturned by a neurologist from the University of Liège. Houben was now considered to have locked-in syndrome, but the author of the article, one Manfred Dworschak, was able to interview him with the assistance of Linda Wouters, a speech therapist.

Wouters stood behind Houben with his right index finger in her hand, and took the small faltering movements it made as cue for intentioned communication, which she then assisted him in the performance of, on a keypad.

An announcement was made, echoing through the enclosed air, and I lifted my head better to listen – I cannot say why I must look in order to listen – and watched as I did so from the gallery above the concourse the people moving with intent and purpose between two points, as if they were vectors. It was not my flight, and so I turned back to the story.

I read how Houben's brain, starved of oxygen immediately after the crash which stopped his heart, was found by Steven Laureys, the neurologist who reassessed him nearly a quarter century later, to have normative functionality. Unlike Jean-Dominique Bauby, the celebrated author of *The Diving Bell and the Butterfly*, a memoir written solely through the use of his left eyelid, the only part of his body which, following a stroke, he could voluntarily move, Rom Houben could move no part of himself with sufficient control to enable communication. From the moment of Laureys' reassessment on, twenty-three years after he had been abandoned as beyond hope, the neurologist's team devoted all their efforts to attempting to enable him to negotiate the walls of this cave which he himself had become. Although Houben could not move his hands or feet with sufficient control to communicate, he was clearly conscious and full of a desire for the world. There exists footage – which, as soon as I returned from Berlin, I obtained – taken in the care home where Rom Houben lives in which the nurses carry on with their work while M. Houben sits slumped, curled and twisted up in his chair like a cadaver found in a peat bog, an inaccessible, unintentionable thing. As soon as his mother enters the room and speaks, however, his body lurches up. He is reanimated. By explosive force of its desires, the specimen is capable of blasting through the dead pathways into the motors of its physical self. The motion is not noble or meaningful; it does not even appear human. But that is how it is most powerfully significant: to watch Rom Houben's reaction to his mother's voice is to witness an instinctual love, to observe how powerful desire can be to propel such an apparently impossible crossing, as if from an alternative universe to our own, or the bursting of life out of inanimacy. And if that word is made up, then all the better, because it is a miracle.

Laureys' team, understanding that the patient could move and respond to stimuli in accordance with the desires of his consciousness, eventually discovered that he could communicate through the intermediary of a facilitative communicator, in this case Linda Wouters. Holding just one finger, Wouters was able to sense Houbens' desired movement, and exert the control he himself could not, typing answers into a specially designed keyboard. All of a sudden the language poured forth from this man who had been submerged in the cave of himself for nearly a quarter of a century. Asked how he survived this time trapped within his own thoughts, his consciousness entirely unknown to the dozens, perhaps hundreds of people who ministered to his bodily needs while he lay in the nursing home, considered a mere pair of unseeing eyes mounted in flesh and bone and little else, Houben said, 'I meditated, I dreamed that I was somewhere else.' Able only to watch and listen, he became in his own words 'an expert on human relations'. Asked whether he was angry at the staff in the care home or the doctors who misdiagnosed him, Houben said no, but he admits, when praising his family, that the staff, by daily familiarity with inert form, soon saw him as little more than a mound of thoughtless flesh.

In the article in *Der Spiegel*, I read the words of Rom Houben with wonder.

'I am called Rom. I am not dead. The nurses came, they patted me, they sometimes took my hand, and I heard them say "no hope". I meditated, I dreamed my life away – it was all I could do. I don't want to blame anyone – it wouldn't do any good. But I owe my life to my family. Everyone else gave up.'

He speaks of how he kept himself occupied:

'I studied what happened around me as if it were a tiny piece of world drama, the bizarre peculiarities of the other patients in the common room, the entry of the doctors into my room, the gossip of the nurses who were not embarrassed to speak about their boyfriends in front of "the extinct one". That made me an expert on relationships.'

Perhaps he sounds in these words like a blandly heroic individual, but such a judgment would surely be unfair. How should we – how would you – speak after a quarter century of silence? Is there enough weight to words, any words, adequately to impact upon the consciousness of the listener the incomparable experience of being marooned within the cave of yourself for twenty-three years? My own response to the story when I first read of it in the airport at Berlin I find to be curiously opposite to that which I have for it now.

Another noise came – this time the sound of a baggage truck reversing – and I looked up from the page again to see exactly what had been there before: the enormous board detailing departures and arrivals, the trolley dock, the gates with their neatly turned-out assistants (somewhat like the Swiss guard at the gates to the Vatican, I realised) at their portals, and the conveyor belts at their sides, and, again, the people moving with purpose from one place to another. This time, though, a feeling flooded into me as if I were empty, a feeling which I can only describe as chemical: it entered into me from some gland in my brain, and proceeded to diffuse through a body which until then I had considered to be made of solid matter but which I now conceived to be entirely hollow, like a cavern, but one whose walls were as dry and fibrous as blotting paper. My hands shook, I felt sweat cover my entire torso, and a hot prickle ran up my neck and scalp. I was in that moment certain that I was going to die, and so I made for the toilet so that I could do so, if not in dignity, then at least in private. I stayed in the cubicle, immersed in a terrible fear, for what seemed to be many hours; but when eventually the episode ended and I flipped the latch and came out, the airport remained suffused with white weightless light, the people still moving endlessly. I had not even missed my flight. Exhausted, I went to my gate, and from here the memory fades: I cannot recall the journey thenceforward, neither even the airline, nor whether I took the train from Stansted back home, or if I had parked in Long Stay.

The appalling twist to the story of Rom Houben came six months later, when it was discovered that Linda Wouters, Rom Houben's bridge to the lived world, was not in fact taking dictation from him by the minute movements of his finger but was instead inventing the whole story herself. A blind study revealed without any doubt that Houben's answers were not his own. All it took was to ask him questions through headphones without Wouters being able to hear; either the answer made no sense in context, or there was no answer at all. Wouters became the object of bile and vilification in such a manner that has since become the stock and accepted response to anything which appears to be not to our liking. However, even as Rom Houben was subsequently pushed back into the cave of himself by this revelation, again to become undiscoverable, a new and even more intriguing element to the story became visible: Linda Wouters truly believed that she was undertaking her purported role. The strength of her desire to bring Rom Houben back to the living in language, much like Rom's own desire to make communication with his mother, caused a bursting forth, a leap across the impossible. To parse the bounding lines between faith, delusion, truth, love, desire – it is the work of a lifetime, of every lifetime.

The peculiar thing is, that when I think of Rom Houben now, ten years after first learning of him – particularly before his rediscovery, cocooned there for twenty-three years in absolute silence and rest like a fossil – I cannot help but feel a longing to be plunged into that state, never to be found, to simply have the mechanism of my mind wind down like a clock through time into shapeless oblivion.

★

—I pursued the true velocity of my spinning with every means available, and it is true that a gram of speed mixed as best as one can into a pint of water (so as not to corrupt the voice of one's singing), along with a drop of liquid acid and a lung of skunk smoke, performs wonders for the sustenance of the hunter. I saw the centre of myself as the turning of a lighthouse across the peaked sea, the gallop of a fine horse across the steppe, the treading of footsteps in ancient mud. For many years I thrust out through time and made play with the motes of being. But then, when it was deemed, when it was that I, happened didn't I, to, seeing too much, – they filled me didn't they with this terrorball, awfall woollen antithought, and my spinning lost all its coltish tautness, and I was domesticated to myself, a me-cow feeding upon the grass of myself, and there was nothing to think or feel.

Let me say out the ways of this obscene chemical cosh.

Before: interminable spinning, ferocity-in-velocity, pins and pricks of immediate light, all musics well dressed quarter-to-quarter by the adze of feelingful logic, crimson, lime, the fragrance of warmwet ferns, most elevated, effervescence-in-efflorescence, singings of bright birds, the infinite play of things apprehended from beneath even the meanest bush, shadows not but burstings of light.

After: and I went go to I went to the side to the side by where there where the side for the white to go to find to side the white the white bread I find I found took out with hand slice the slice of white bread took out the bag long bag the white bread long square bag of the white bread my hand I went to go there for the white bread into there where found put my hand where there I had went into the long square bag where the bread I had went for getting the bread square into my own hand the hand in my hand the bread out from the bag into the air where my mouth is into my mouth the white bread the square no square changed by my mouth bite into the square not square now chew make myself into white into the white bread square no bite out of into the bag like the white bread there where I had gone there where the white bread not even hungry.

That is what I was, and what I became, and so don't go saying, No, you mustn't kill yourself, because there is no moral or duty to the preservation of such a life as that.

★

I found travelling at the fringe of the sea in the coastal bus to have a soothing effect on my nerves. I began to take the train up to Sheringham, Cromer or Yarmouth several times each week, where I would then board the coasthopper and sit on the seaward side of the aisle and look at the scenery for two hours one way and two hours back. I took to stopping at Mundesley at a cafe popular with cyclists for cake, after which I would return to the bus stop and wait for my journey to continue on a different though identical bus. Sometimes I would head further west to Wells-next-the-Sea. There I invariably walked along the mile-long dyke which runs beside the East Fleet and then over the perfect sands of Wells beach, where the terns and warblers negotiated the wind to land and feed, and where boats which seemed far too large to do so passed within just a few metres of the beach along a channel dredged weekly so that the harbour remained accessible. One day the bus stopped in Blakeney and, seeing a sign for a crab shed there, I decided to take a chance on the village. I left the main coastal road, which was noisy with traffic, as soon as I could, and soon found myself moving along the quay beside the river Glaven and looking out across the salt marshes which ran out to the sea edge. The houses and garden walls, as is the tradition throughout north Norfolk, were clad in small flints closely packed in lime mortar, and as I walked at their side I noticed for the first time with immense pleasure how this multitude of little protrusions from the walls altered the sounds of voices, gull calls and passing cars, making them seem softer and somehow more intimately involved in my progress. At the shack, I bought a platter of crab, and continued on to the guildhall where, walking in its vaulted brick undercroft, I experienced a sudden premonition that this six-hundred-year-old building would collapse on me, and was compelled to leave. I walked up the hill towards the church, where, passing the cemetery and seeing the statuary, I recalled a fact which had amused me when I first heard it, that the masons of sixteenth-century Italy prefabricated multiple tombstones, complete with statuary depicting the deceased, though the faces remained, for the time being, unhewn, featureless blocks. Here, five hundred years ago, the pressures of capital were already at play, and the solution neat. At the point of purchase, all the mason then had to do was take out his chisel and take away all excess material which prevented the stone from doing its job, and the family was satisfied with a likeness. It was only now that I wondered what model the stonemason would work from. Would he be brought the body of the deceased into his workshop? Or would the face of a family member, chosen for the similarity, be good enough for the task? Either way, it pleased me for some perverse reason that, half a millennium ago, such streamlined practises were already in place in the business of the dead.

The cemetery was like a city, having an old quarter crowded with leaning stones haphazardly piled up next to each other, overgrown, with birds, squirrels and insects undertaking their daily chores, and a modern end, where the graves were identical, with plots as evenly spaced as if those of a caravan park, and the flowers were cut instead of wild. Both had a beauty to them. I wandered between the stones and read the names and dates of the people buried there and I remembered a statistic I had read somewhere that less than five per cent of British people can name a single one of their great-grandparents. Why we should expect anything other than a similar oblivion for ourselves, I don't know, but we surely do.

The friend who had told me of the Italian stonemasons – a lecturer in history whose specialist area had somehow become conceptions and representations of death – also informed me, as one among many audience members at a public lecture, of Johannes Schenck von Grafenberg, a largely forgotten doctor of medicine at the Albert-Ludwigs-Universität at Freiburg im Breisgau, whose *Monstrorum historia memorabilis*, published in 1609, was written at least in part in response to the zealous pursuit by residents both within the city and beyond of the burning of witches in the latter half of the sixteenth century.

By indefatigable medical investigation, von Grafenberg – so my friend began – gained some degree of insight into the mutations to which the human body is prone, just as he had investigated aberrances of human cognition caused by injury to the head, though of course the genetics of mutation was a treasurehouse inaccessible to him. The brutal murder of innocent young women and men (the conventional collocation is inverted by the statistics: the victims were overwhelmingly women) which von Grafenberg thought his researches might help to eradicate, however, was encouraged by the influx of such strange specimens of humanity as came to the city from all over the Rhineland to queue outside the door of his house every first Monday of the month. At these times the guesthouses of the town would all be found mysteriously closed, the shutters forbidding even so much as a knock, and the disfigured visitors to the town would often be forced to sleep in the street if Doctor von Grafenberg's stables were already filled by those who had been forewarned of the town's hostility and arrived before the previous dawn to avoid it. As elsewhere, the customary treatment of witches in von Grafenberg's little town was death by burning, a means by which a triple benefit could be procured; namely, punishment of the malefactor, eradication of his or her evil spirit, and the disposal of the body which had housed it in a way conducive to public health, a point of civic concern on which the city still prides itself today, as can be seen (and here my friend elicited a little purring chuckle from the audience) by the environmental education work of the BUND-Oekostation. Some of those arriving in the town and seeking to become von Grafenberg's patients never succeeded in obtaining treatment for their deformities, becoming instead prey to this fanaticism for witches.

Neither inability nor unwillingness to read an entire volume of Renaissance medicine written in Latin need stand in your way (so my friend continued, eyeing the audience as if seeking out her own students), for the book was published with copious illustrations, several of which we shall look at today. Among these can be found numerous examples of children born living, with protuberances from, and deformities of, the head; or else with features resembling those more normally belonging to a dog, wolf, hare, donkey or frog. Numerous plates show twins of varying degrees of conjunction, ranging from the appearance of two fully formed human infants able to stand, move and speak as if there was nothing out of the ordinary about them (though always at intersection one with another); to single individuals exhibiting all the appearance of normality except for the presence of an extra leg or arm, or even in some cases a second head protruding from the abdomen.

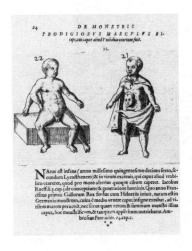

In truth it has been known, as von Grafenberg recorded in his pioneering work, for a body to inhabit another so completely that the former be fully enclosed within its twin, invisible to the eye of even the most experienced medical practitioner. The capabilities of witchcraft, in the face of an aberrant and experimental nature, are discovered to be wanting. Cases abound, from von Grafenberg up to the present day, of patients of all ages being admitted for the treatment of cysts and tumours which are found only after invasive surgery to be a human twin housed within themselves. Invariably these 'twins' are not recognisably human, but are instead only underdeveloped portions of a foetus. Many are calcified deposits, and are drawn out of flesh like fossils from the ground. In one example from 2008, though, there was found inside the abdomen of a two-month-old girl a foetus which, though only partially formed, was flesh, and exhibited a hand complete with digits.

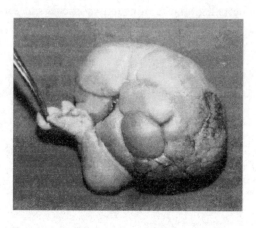

One of the earliest reliable records of such a discovery can be found in George William Young's essay 'Case of a Foetus Found in the Abdomen of a Boy', published in 1808, in which the author gives a detailed account of the discovery inside John Hare, born only six months before, of a twin sibling which, after months of suffering, had killed its host. In Young's essay we are informed of the three visits John and his mother made to him, and the desperate worry which consumed John's mother when, in ebbs and flows like a tide, her son's abdomen swelled up to grotesque proportions until he expelled vast quantities of foul green liquid from his mouth, and was given another month's reprieve, until the next time. The boy continued to gain weight, but it was not his own; he became pale, almost see-through, and emaciated, while the growth in his stomach increased in strength and size until, eventually, he died. When Young opened little John Hare's abdomen up he was astonished to discover the presence within of a portion of a sibling which, clinging to his liver, had fed off the blood supply of his big brother until he killed them both.

In one extreme instance, my friend continued to an audience both appalled and enraptured, a man living in Augustów in eastern Poland who reported in 1996 to the Ogólny hospital complaining of a distended and painful abdomen soon began exhibiting symptoms of hepatic encephalopathy, and was taken through to theatre. Here, doctors made exploratory incisions beneath the patient's ribcage to the right and were amazed to discover a small, perfectly formed hand pushing from within the pericardium. The chief surgeon, Klotylda Jaworska, came immediately. Less than nine hours later a little female human, although necessarily still attached by the abdomen to the blood supply of her brother by a small branch from the coeliac trunk, was brought to inhabit the world on the exterior of what appeared to be her male mother; though, as with John Hare, owing to their sharing his blood supply, of course she could not be detached from him. Curiously enough, this sister of the patient, subsequently named after the surgeon who had delivered her, and who was brought into the world as if his daughter, had on her face, beneath the left eye, a little birthmark precisely that same shape and tone of one which could be found on the face of her host's mother. This was the first thing which the patient, whose name was Filip, decided he would tell his mother when he himself had recovered from the shock of having a living person removed from within himself and thenceforth attached to his right side, conceiving this information to be the one thing which might possibly persuade her to believe him, though he knew this to be impossible in view of her sceptical bent. Nevertheless, he walked to the payphone at the entrance to the ward, with his sister sat in a specially designed sling above his right hip, and he dialled their mother's number. However, in the five days during which the two patients recuperated, never did he manage to speak with her. It was only when Filip and Klotylda were discharged that he discovered their mother had not been seen since the night of his admittance to hospital, and in his and his sister's subsequent long life they never did discover where their mother had gone, though it would happen every once in a while that Filip would look at the birthmark beneath his sister-daughter's face and be convinced that he had given birth to the mother who herself had borne him.

★

You sit beside me, even across me, half inside, wherever I am, and you hold my hand, and you make me speak, and here I am now, telling these tales. Everything is desire. Sometimes you will speak back, with hushed voice, conciliatory. Sometimes you will tear back into the past with the same words you used then, persuaded you were intentionally destroyed. You were never my twin but it feels as if that is how it must have been. Either way, it is all just desire. Stories grow out of me like branches from the trunk of a tree, and if they are later grown round and leave such obdurate knots within that one day the timber of me will be useful for nothing but firewood, then that's life – or death.

—Understand that this is and has always been the way, and was then, when I came to the crux of it, my tree, where the dream was transacted:

I know that I hung there, nine nights, down in the hollow, where the water slows, there, from the windless tree. I ebbed indeed from myself, lap lap. Sometimes I was within myself, full of outrage and resistance, and then sometimes I was without, though also within, among the dense and good woodness of the tree, all calm. I travelled between the two places, not places, but something else entirely, like smoke all at once discovering itself capable of penetrating the surface of a mirror, revealing the fallacy of edges and planes, waiting, but not waiting, until all necessary negotiations had been made.

★

—People will say that I am mad that this is an impossibility but I know as they should that nothing is an impossibility on this earth which in truth a person may one day sink into never to emerge and be burned by the fires of molten rock which are turned by the spinning ball at its centre to become nothing but ash and a few knots of scorched bone.

 —I was conceived as his twin, and he mine, —

 (This is not true – never were we twins – but this hectoring voice asserts it anyway, from somewhere.)

      —but by wily trickery and the fault of my innocence was led into a fibrous thicket and deposited there to be lost in howlings with no means of escape from that labyrinth only left to sit in loneliness and loss like one fishing the Styx while he slunk off and emerged into that light and fanfare. Twenty-one months I sat there in grief not for myself but for him, feeling but not yet knowing the truth of this abandonment evil beyond the pale. In the end my grief coalesced into something for which there is no word and I entered into the channels of the labyrinth. With each new turn I was further enmeshed, more lost with each step two further from life but by the fire of my innocent intellect I burned my way out. Didn't then he know it when by the sweet logic of that innocent intellect I negotiated the singular dangerous way up out of the netherworld, picking the lock of physical becoming and screaming entered into living hands and legs reaching out with hunger for experience my voice shrill and eager to make shape this is what it is to be born with a true soul. And yet my other my adversary he had thirteened the time against my ever innocence and brought the snow down to fill the streets against my egress and back into the home you had labyrinthed also against. That brother worm thing slunk in corners in shadows poisoning himself with twisted jealousies and could not even look with eyes even in approach to my cot. And did you not when finally capable to approach the cot hit me across my head with a little toy bat, big brother?

*

So deeply was I immersed in these thoughts and others like them that it was not until a fat drop hit me on the crown of my head that I realised the sky had become almost completely dark two hours earlier than was customary at this time of year, and a rainstorm, which must have been heading in from the sea for some time, was about to commence. In addition to this, although it could not be explained by my general indolence during the day – I had merely caught two buses and wandered around Blakeney a little – I discovered myself to be exhausted. I therefore resolved to spend the night in the village if it could be managed. Accordingly, I made enquiries, and soon was pleased to find myself booked into a room above the local pub, which, although appearing to serve poor food at worse prices, had the benefit of being warm and cosy in a way that modernised and renovated establishments never are. Showering, I pulled back on my old clothes and felt more refreshed than I imagined would have been possible. And so it was that I went down to the bar to gain more intimate knowledge of the state of the food there, and though I did not know it yet, to discover, from another diner within the pub, all about a man called Servington Savery, a great and forgotten early English experimenter in magnetism.

My fellow guest, who from the sound and demeanour of him seemed to live permanently within the establishment – who perhaps was the black sheep relative of those who worked the bar and kitchen, and whom these industrious individuals were forced to tolerate (by all appearances he seemed to be in that wonderful phrase *not all there*) because the deeds were in his name – yes, this fellow guest who seemed to be no guest at all wasted no opportunity in seeking out a seat beside me in order that he might be allowed to talk with someone who had not yet built up methods of resistance against his unwanted advances. As the storm outside constructed itself and made a rage of the air, this man gave me a potted history of the pub and the surrounding area before the conversation got onto the notable people who had come through the doors – none of whom I had ever heard.

By some cause or other this conversation, if that is what it could be called, caught on a man called Servington Savery, whose experiments in magnetism proved the hypotheses of William Gilbert's *De Magnete*, published one hundred and thirty years earlier, including that the earth was magnetised. This Savery did by driving a ferrous crook into the ground and dangling a nail from its perpendicular portion. He discovered that it clung. Savery, my new friend informed me, presented his findings in a most sober and sensible fashion (which, it seemed, was not in accordance with his habitual temperament) to the Royal Society towards the end of the third decade of the eighteenth century. Upon the publication of his 'Magnetical Observations & Experiments' on the first day of 1730 he declared that day, in a letter to the woman who soon would become his wife, to be 'a most Sweet opening to the year for your Savery'. My dinner companion and I visited many people in our conversation – all of whom, though their world was no longer ours, this peculiar individual spoke about as if they were still living – and yet, when time was called and I made my way to the strange world of my rented single bed, it was Servington Savery who remained at the forefront of my thought, and who must have occupied also my dreams, because, when, waking the next morning, I parted the curtains and looked down from the window to the old stables at the end of the garden, the first thing I thought of was Savery and how this must have been the building he had used for a laboratory during his extended stay in Norfolk. Being one who at this time was thankful for any distraction which could be obtained to fill the days, I felt a curious and no doubt childish desire to visit the place where this man of whose existence I had had no knowledge at all twenty-four hours before had done his last work.

So it was that I went down to the bar and requested permission to go into the place, which was quizzically given. Of course, when the doors into the little building were opened for me I found myself to be walking on concrete, surrounded by plastic crates and sacks of dry goods, beneath a hanging polystyrene ceiling of only several decades' age at most, and the walls had been pointed so zealously that all the many flints from which it was constructed were fully ensconced in the surrounding mortar, like a series of bluffs only just managing to sustain their protrusion above an expanse of sheer floodwater. There was no sign of any former use. Indeed, the building seemed so recently built that I would have taken it as confirmation of my suspicions that my dinner companion of the night before had been making it all up, had I not seen, at the very last moment, even as the bartender brought the double doors together after my departure, the number '1708' inscribed on a stone at the apex of the roof immediately beneath the gable. Owing to the custom for commemorative stones to face outwards, it must have been inadvertently turned around to face the dark interior during one of the building's periodic periods of restoration and repair.

This confirmation of the veracity of my dinner companion's stories – which, of course, was no confirmation at all – allowed Savery to move out of myth into the everyday world. And so, taking the breakfast I ordered up to my room, I went over the details I had been given the night before. Savery, after his initial success with the Royal Society, had the invitation with which he concludes his article – to readily communicate the success of a design for the refinement of the compass – ignored, perhaps owing to rumour of his eccentricities, and he continued to work, through the 1730s, on the production of the first compound magnet in Devon, the county of his birth, where he remained for almost all of his life, except for that ending he made of it in Norfolk. It was during this time that Savery became the principal partner to one Gowin Knight, a physicist, whose skill lay more in deception than science and who is, as a result, now erroneously credited with discovering the process by which strongly magnetised steel could be produced. Savery, spurned by the Royal Society and betrayed by his business partner, felt a great loathing for the red earth, quick hills and deep green tummocks of his home, and so drove his young family across the country to the flatlands of Norfolk. Here, he set up a laboratory for his latter investigations into the structure and provenance of the earth, only coming out when he was called in for meals from the house – by use of an ingenious device constructed of multiple pieces of piped sacking sewn end to end, a ball bearing and a bell – or, at night, if his candle guttered.

After a time, and an increasing interest in the function of the brain, he befriended one of the stockboys from the local farmhouse and, using an assemblage of the magnets which he had made as prototypes for Gowin Knight, began to undertake experiments on the effects of magnetism on perception. Savery was convinced that the earth had at its centre a hot and dense ball of iron and zinc which span at incredible velocity – a conviction which has of course since been proven correct – and that the earth, like the thrumming brain of a human, generates consciousness generally, and desire particularly, by the rotational aspect of that which spins at its centre. The local boy whom Savery befriended, a Thomas Webb, was placed in a chair adapted for the purpose of experimentation with a cage holding a helmet-like object at its centre, which could be lowered with the use of a lever down around the subject's head, and whose magnets, placed into clasps within the helmet running along incrementally marked rails, much like a model representing the planets of the solar system, could be turned three hundred and sixty degrees in three dimensions in respect to the centre point of the helmet, their sun, which in point of fact must have been the very core of Webb's brain. The meticulous Savery, being thereby capable of making minute adjustments to the positions of the magnets with the use of the helmet, recorded his results.

Webb, both of whose parents had died in his infancy, and who had been brought up on the Wiveton farm where his mother had been a dairymaid, was, in the words of Savery (as my dinner companion related to me), a melancholy pale shivering thing, though gentle and indulgent, particularly with the animals he tended and with whom he slept in their barn. 'I have a mind to take him in myself,' Savery once wrote in a letter to his sister-in-law, 'but that the loss of companionship with the beasts he counts his most intimate friends would likely spell the terminance of what thread of life is left in him.'

The care and consideration which Savery exhibits in his letters for the orphan boy is entirely absent in the logbook in which he kept records of his experiments, and in which we find such entries as: 'Aug. 14th 1742. W. in chair 4hrs. Mag. 240°x95°. Vomiting.' and '5th Mar' '43: 11 hrs. resonance & finial trails. promising. Tears after.' The transit of the moon, like the ebb and flow of the tide it is responsible for (so my dinner companion said in one of his many asides, asides which might appear at first to be digressions, but become mirrors to the whole as we move on), is entirely predictable in the future, and so too entirely recallable. Savery's experiments were conducted, at least at first, in accordance with the phases of the moon. He believed that the gravitational pull of the earth was a kind of womb-force, that it was the source of all love, and that the moon was a lost twin of the earth, one which had arisen from it without precedent or explanation, like Athena from the head of Zeus.

In the winter of 1744, a discovery of some kind must have been made, because Savery and Webb equipped two horses with supplies sufficient for a week's travel, placed the chair in a cart behind the great inquisitor of magnetism, as if it were the throne of Science him- or herself, and made an appalling journey through all the indignities a freezing February could treat them to, from Blakeney, through Holt, Aylsham and North Walsham, down to the boggy peat marshes and water channels of the Broads, where they camped for four days of experimentation. Although no reason is given for this translocation of Savery's experiments, it seems that he believed the thick layers of peat might act as an insulator from the magnetism of the centre of the earth. Deep in the middle of nowhere a wheel came loose from their wagon and bounced down the dyke with joyful bounding leaps. After a replacement was obtained from a cartwright at Thurne, Savery took his boy and the experimenting chair to the most remote part of the peat bed he could find.

By the time they finally arrived at their destination, Savery and Webb had been shrouded in fog, pelted by hail, or soaked by a drizzle whose consistency and capacity for making one wet is well known to anyone who has ever visited Norfolk in winter. Wild horses, as if skilled in a secret power of incarnation, emerged out of the vapours to observe the experimenting pair, and made equally unheralded returns into the immaterial gloom, the thick air turning in twin scrolls behind to swallow them up. Webb, wearing two of everything, and four of gloves and socks, sat in the chair whose leather seat, over the months of their experimentation, had so taken on the shape of his buttocks as to have become a perfect resting place, and had the magnets applied most proximate to those places of his brain which tended towards greatest affect. Servington Savery walked over the soggy ground, felt the body of it quiver like flesh beneath each foot tread, wiped the drips from his nose onto the sleeve of his oilcloth longcoat, and fell into step with the movements of the hand of his chronometer, upon which his eyes were perpetually fixed. Every thirty minutes he returned to Webb and took record of his sensory experience, recording such things as 'buzzing s'ation r. temple' and 'glaucus, or fog.?' After three hours, the wind rose, the fog was plaited into wreaths, lifted like a wing, was borne away altogether, and Servington Savery returned to make observations of his subject only to find that his subject was entirely unobservable: Webb had vanished, leaving only an empty chair.

When finally he found Webb, some two hundred yards away, and a good ten minutes later, Savery's anger dissipated just as had the fog as soon as he saw that the boy, against all the dictates of possibility, was enclosed within a small hollow in the peat, half drowned in the brackish black water, with an aperture of only several inches wide opening out to the air for him to breathe through.

What had happened?

He did not know.

How had he got here?

He could not remember.

All over the peaty earth long spines of saltwater grass and delicate moss grew. The particular constellation enclosing Webb must have been formed many years ago, probably decades or centuries, perhaps millennia – more, into the deep inconceivable – and yet here was this boy, Mr Thomas Webb, orphan and former stockboy of Wiveton dairy farm, now assistant to the illustrious experimenter Servington Savery, enclosed within.

The peaty earth was thick and heavy, and Savery being no longer what he was, Webb was finally only freed from his fleshly enclosure late that evening. Throughout the ordeal he remained silent on the subject of what had happened, either because he still could not remember or because what came back to him was too disturbing to disclose while he was still half-swallowed by the ground. They slept at Horning in beds for the first time in a week, and it was here that Webb described what had happened, how the figure he had first sensed through the laboratory walls in their early experiments at Shilstone had, out here, in the peat bogs, been free to approach him out of the fog, but how tentatively it came, appearing half-substantiate, then uncoiling into the mist, or else riding as a baggage upon one of the wild horses only to slip off as she shied, turned and dipped back into the whiteness. With time the intensity increased, however, until a figure came out to him, across the empty gap of air between the fog and the unguessable point of himself at the centre.

Hadn't his master the great inquisitor of magnetism said that at the centre of the earth there was a spinning ball of iron so big and dense that it boiled the oceans of iron and nickel within which it floated, the way the brand did the water in the bucket, though not once but forever? That the mineral crust on the surface of the ironmonger's water was no different to the little congealed part of the earth which supported them all? It did not seem right to be drawing things across that divide, and yet here strode his father, unbraided from the fog, divested of baggagement, brandishing a knife with a brace of grouse at his belt, and all he could smell was the sour sharpness a hoof or hair has to its burning.

Savery spared the young Webb from further experimentation, and turned all his attentions thenceforth to himself. What remains of his story is a patchwork of clues at best (so it was that my dinner companion had told me the night before), but it is certain that he scheduled a bark out from Wells-next-the-Sea several months later, in May, when the weather had become more clement, with the intention of continuing his experiments, though this time out at sea, as a companion piece or flipside of research to that conducted on the thick blanket of peat with Webb. The boat, which it seems Savery had chosen carefully, or perhaps named himself, for it was called *Lodestone*, was rented on 14 May 1745, and was found two weeks later drifting off the little West Frisian island of Terschelling with no one aboard. Conditions had been good throughout the month, there was no damage to the boat, and there was a plentiful supply of food and water. The assumption made by the English authorities, against all refutations of his wife, was that Savery must for some reason or other have taken his own life. However, it is clear from the record of his notebook, which was found in the cabin, that Savery was entirely consumed with the belief that he was about to make a breakthrough in his studies. Such was his enthusiasm in the last few entries in his notebook that his usual meticulous neatness of hand and sober use of language is disrupted by exclamations such as 'Will be upon us soon!' and 'Drag strong. Cavern(?) What is meaning.'

'Normally,' said my dinner companion – it seems strange now that I never thought to discover his name – 'a body going overboard will wash up somewhere sometime soon, or be picked up, ballooned up they never do sink, but Servington Savery's body was never found.'

I was left to ponder the significance of this for a time as he went to the bar once again to check for messages (who could it be, I wondered, that he was waiting for a message from?) In fact no conclusion to the story was offered, even though the set-up had most clearly been put in place with intention (a glittering eye and multiple interruptions and digressions were the techniques used). In the end I had to content myself with the assumption that my storyteller implied that Savery had found himself translocated by the powers of magnetism which he had harnessed to a place if not within the waters, for still his body would have been found, then by logical if unreasonable necessity beneath them, within the seabed, where perhaps he could still be found if only we knew how and where to dig.

And I wondered, against the pressure of my mind's desire, whether it is sufficient, when it comes down to it, to think of the dead across time? Or must acts be undertaken, makings inside time, burrowings into the present, in order that the ball should be kept ever spinning? And then, although it may seem a strange delusion particular to our species to commemorate our dead with acts and objects when we know that all they become is the elemental world around us, this transformation into the raw ore of what the world will make next, whichever way it is considered, is more magical than any of the accounts the religions have dreamed up.

The next morning I came down from my little room to check out, and saw in the lanes as I left all about me the remnants of the storm the night before – broken branches in the roads, hedges choked with rubbish, floods in the elbows of the lanes, and the sky swept clear and clean by the now distant wind. I walked along the dyke, up to the beach, where, as I began walking along the ancient pebble spit of Blakeney Point, I was astonished to find that the whole beach had been transformed in the course of a single storm from a colossus of pebbles into sand and shingle, a feat which must have involved the movement of millions upon millions of tons of material up from the seabed and onto the land, no doubt some of it having its origin in the cliffs at Happisburgh, and before that in the banks of the ancient and lost Bytham which had flowed out to the sea there, and even perhaps a little of which had edged the footprints of that particular family which had walked the delta a million years ago, the trace of whom we saw for a flicker of time, and then was again gone.

HORSES

I n the spring of the following year, when everything beyond my window was slowly coming back to life – even, or especially so, the light – I came to the realisation that the insomnia which had illuminated everything in me, as if my mind were an Arctic summer, was gone. My cave under the sea, too, had closed up. Perhaps it was deemed that I no longer required it, though by whom I could not say. In any case, I was compelled from that moment to inhabit only the surface of this cold terranean world just like any other creature – excepting of course the birds (*Come, great dark bird*) – exiled from the pleasantness of my wandering night-thoughts and the cave's warm and liquid interior. Long days I sat in my bedroom, in a chair I had brought upstairs and placed close by the old sash window, and watched the light develop in the sky. Here, I would simply think.

Some unaccountable movement in myself led me to avoid the downstairs rooms of the house; I had to be elevated, able to see the roofs of the terraces wind unevenly up the incline of the streets like the vertebrae of an immense creature which had died long ago. I discovered myself capable of sitting in that chair for hours on end, transported into distant pasts, many of which – perhaps most – never existed. At such times as the loose forms of this activity seemed to draw into a loop, I would sometimes pick up a book to read, but only first thing in the morning was I capable of sustaining any degree of attention. Invariably, in the middle of the afternoon I would drop into a deep sleep and be shocked to find, when I came round again, that what felt to have been a period of unimaginable extension, many hundreds of years, was only a matter of half an hour or so, a short enough span of time for the light and its attendant shadow outside to have moved so little as to be indistinguishable, and that this thing we call civilisation persisted around me.

This state of living could have continued, as far as I was concerned, indefinitely. I had everything I needed, if not entirely in the house, then only a short walk away. For the sake of my health, I had begun in the previous winter to force myself to take brief excursions beyond these four walls, even if only a single turn about the line of terraces that ran inside the loop of my road and the next. I drank strong coffee and kept the house cold. Then, as if it was the simplest thing of all, the springtime had come – your time of year, when you came into and left the world, most simply, as if through no more than a door – and the birds are found to be capable still of singing (*Come, come, great dark birds*) and the light is altered, if only for a while.

I examined myself, and discovered that I was in fact happy, or at least not discontented. Dread and terror had moved out and on to reside with some other poor soul. I did not reflect on the fact that I hadn't had a conversation with another human for close to a year. Nor that the springtime seemed to be bursting out of every morning anew, as if I were trapped at the threshold of the seasons, and time was bunched up at its seam – I, perhaps, the burr upon which it was snagged.

This was the shape of things when, one day, there was a knock at the door. I descended the stairs, turned into the front room, and then, when my hand had almost reached the latch, the knock came again, and I stopped, understanding by some instinct that the knock did not herald a delivery or cold call – how I had grown to appreciate the cold call – but rather a visit from a friend. This process of comprehension occurring in the space of no more than a moment, I discovered myself to be utterly immobile at its conclusion. Inwardly, I played out pro-testations at this interruption of my day, justifying my resistance to company with recourse to a number of duties which did not exist, and which, even if they had, could in any case have been performed on any other day of the week – or indeed month or year. However, I knew that if I opened the door I would only invite this person in, whoever it was, and pretend I was glad to see them. So it was that I stood there, behind the door, looking at nothing so much as the crawl of time under pressure of this unwanted visit. Just as I thought I might be free to relax, that I would hear the hinges of the gate squeak and foot-tread ascend the hill of my road (the ground here must have hollows in it, just as has much of Norwich from the quarrying of chalk in the eighteenth and nineteenth centuries, for the walk of people outside comes up into the front room in a peculiarly resonant thump) – just when I thought that I might be able to turn and reascend the stairs, the light in the room altered, dimmed, and visible through the window was the familiar face of a friend craning over the shrubbery and looking obliquely at me in my palsied state of indecision. The head disappeared. Whisperings ensued with a companion. The letterbox opened, not to the arced drop of a letter, but to a pair of eyes and a plea for me to open the door, something I could hardly now refuse, having been caught at this shameful inaction.

★

A few months later, in the middle of July, at the height of summer, after discovering that my continued resistance to going anywhere would soon yield a visit made to me – something far worse – I packed a small bag and caught the train to Liverpool Street, the Underground to Paddington, and from there another train to Newbury, where, walking to the bus stop in an attempt to complete my journey to the little village of Woodhay, I tripped and seriously sprained my ankle.

—You're early, he said when I phoned.

I told him about my injury, which seemed faintly to amuse him.

Twenty minutes later he pulled into the car park at Newbury station, threw my little bag in the boot and helped me fold myself into the passenger seat. On the back seat, I saw he had already pulled some crutches out of somewhere.

He – who had pushed his face up against the glass of my front window – and his wife were about to embark on a trip east, across the channel from Hull to Rotterdam, through Münster, Bremen and Hamburg, across Poland along the shore of the Baltic Sea, up to Riga, then through Moscow, across the northern steppe, and into the Urals. They were both secondary school teachers, and had allowed themselves the full six weeks of the summer holiday for their journey. I was to be the caretaker of an old cottage they had recently bought in the North Wessex Downs, and which they had tired of renovating. This was how they managed to persuade me to leave the comfort of my own company – because, in less than a week, it would return, except in a different location.

So it was that, instead of sitting in a chair in my own house, up in my own room, I came to be doing exactly the same in the house of these friends, though overlooking the north Hampshire hills instead of a few lines of terraced roofs in Norwich.

I understood that I had been brought down before my friends' departure for a reason – so that they could, as the phrase ominously goes, 'keep an eye on me' – but they were so preoccupied with tying everything up at work in the final week of the school term, and with preparing for their departure after that, that even when they were at home in the evenings I could mostly sit in silence undisturbed and vanish into my own thoughts, as had become my habit. Still, I cannot deny that I felt a strain in this arrangement, and it was not uncommon for me to enter back into the world and discover these two faces looking at mine in expectation of some kind of response to an unknown query. Or else I caught them exchanging the smallest of glances, detectable nevertheless, which clearly had me for their origin and spoke concern. I might have found the experience a little disconcerting if I had the capacity to dwell on it. As far as I could grasp, though, everything was fine. The only difference I could discern was that I experienced a very specific and hitherto unknown form of pain upon the receipt of any kindness, and so I looked forward to their departure for Russia at least as much as they did themselves.

During the day, while my hosts were at work, I attempted to watch television, but in less time than it took me to figure out how to turn the contraption on I felt a profound distaste for humanity gradually permeate my body, and turned it off again. I went out for brief expeditions into the village, feeling like an unsophisticated and antiquated machine as I hobbled forward between these two poles, but it was hot and exhausting travelling over the ground like this. So it was that I took another chair to another window up beneath the low eaves of this cottage and sat down in thought a hundred and fifty miles west of where I had been doing precisely the same thing since the winter had thawed.

Something, though, was different. For some reason, perhaps because of this change of place, the simple translocation of the body elsewhere, anywhere, the interiors of me would not play along. Where, before, I had been brimful of interior activity; now, having brought myself to this new place, I found that interior to be entirely empty and silent. I craved external stimulus, but I couldn't discover in what. I began re-reading the book I had finished during my journey here, but it did not satisfy. I tried to do some jobs about the house – painting the skirting and window frames, repairing a split floorboard – but my ankle wouldn't let me get into a position which would allow my hands to do the work. I drifted from room to room looking for something to occupy me, and was shocked to discover, after several rounds, that there appeared not to be a single book in the house. The only object of interest I could find was a little wooden travelling chess set with miniature drawers set into its body to house the pieces. When one drawer was pushed, say the one containing the white pieces, the other drawer would open in its mirror image out from the other side of the board, revealing the black. The two were connected by some mechanism or other which I couldn't discover the workings of, but it was pleasing to hold and make perform its little trick. The pieces themselves were tiny, and I wondered how it had been possible to make such small figures out of wood. Each piece had a peg set into its base so that the game could be played under extreme conditions without mishap. Accepting the challenge from myself, I put the board under my arm and hobbled upstairs to my chair.

★

Every morning of that first week in the little house at Woodhay I would find on the other side of my door in the hallway, placed up on a stooltop, a morsel to eat and a thermos of fresh coffee.

The pastries were handmade in the bakery in the next village, and incomparably good. My favourite, I quickly came to discover, held half a skinned apricot glazed with jam in its centre, plump and gelatinous as the yolk of an egg, dusted with cinnamon, and a ring of flaked almonds perfectly toasted in a frame about it. As soon as I heard the front latch click shut, signifying the departure of my friends to work, I would pull myself up to a sitting position, swing my legs round, grab my crutches, haul myself to my good foot and cross the room like Tiny Tim to the door in innocent expectation of today's breakfast treat. Having obtained it, I would return to bed and sit up with my back against the wall and eat it as slowly as I could manage.

I think it was on the third evening of my stay that I mentioned, in as innocent a way as I could manage, the absence of books in the house. My friend and his partner looked at me and then at each other as if they had been set a riddle. It was only after a substantial pause in the conversation that they both remembered that all the books had been put in storage at a relative's until they had finished the floor, something they had still not got round to. There was however (I was told) a pile of books up in the attic which, along with numerous items of furniture and debris, had not been cleared from the house in advance of auction, and had become the unwanted property of the new owners of the house. I expressed a desire to see these books and was greeted the next morning by a note reading 'BE CAREFUL' taped to the top rung of a stepladder in the hallway set up in a point at the hatch above.

Clearly at least one of the previous inhabitants had been an avid equestrian, because up in the loft at least forty of the hundred or so books which I found thrown ignominiously into a broad mound, presumably from the hatch, were related to horses. My fear of horses, shared by my mother, I defend for its basis in rational thought: they are bigger, heavier and more powerful than any person. People, moreover, can be coaxed, cajoled and persuaded by this thing we call language. So it is that I have never gone any further with horses than admiring them from a distance. Hard work though it was with only one good foot, I retrieved these books from the attic in ones and twos, and before lunch the attic was emptied and the books piled up next to my bed.

As I began to read, it was as if I were entering an unvisited country; and I discovered that, though they may have no spoken language of their own, horses certainly have acquired a vast human vocabulary dedicated to their parts, forms, behaviours, history, genealogy, value, and so on. Working in the corrugated iron scriptorium he had built in his backyard, with hundreds of words coming in on slips by public appeal every day, James Murray, the editor of the *Oxford English Dictionary*, saw that it was the technical language of English which was the burgeoning category of his time. To think now, nearly one hundred and fifty years later, of all that has changed, all the technological developments that have required their lexicons of names for the people who work within those specialist areas to be able to develop the instruments and machines of our world – even though many merely recycle the old forms into new contexts or combinations – James Murray would have had an even harder time making sense of it all in his tin shed. Such deep quarries of specialised vocabulary are continually being dug out of language that it would come as no surprise if sinkholes started opening up all around us, and the linguistic ground upon which we walk, or talk, collapsed entirely – just as have several such holes have opened up in Norwich over the years, in one case leaving a bus at a forty-five-degree angle half in the ground, as if having attempted for some reason to burrow down into the earth to escape from the human realm – leaving only rubble, mess, fragments of sound incapable, by the excess of signification to which they had been pushed, of meaning anything at all. Through that long summer holiday I read book after book which treated of horses: Charles Montague's *Recollections of an Equestrian Manager* from 1881; *An Equestrian Epistle in Verse*, a poem written for the Earl of Jersey by Thomas Matthias in 1796; *Horse and Rider* from 1950, in which the history of the horse painting is summarised and interrogated; an 1802 edition of *Astley's System of Equestrian Education, Exhibiting the Beauties and Defects of the Horse*; a book on equestrian sports, which I forget the name of, which lays out in exhaustive detail the rules for all varieties of polo; and so on. The sun swung daily over the fields beyond my window, and I read book after book on a subject which a few weeks before I had never even considered.

If I am honest, most of the books in the attic were not very interesting at all. But I did find it calming to hear the voices which spoke their words come through into the present from many decades – sometimes centuries – past. Moreover, I felt an obscure and curious sense of duty to the books which I had rescued from the ignoble heap in the loft above my head: this was probably the last opportunity they would have to be read, destined as they were to be burned a few months from now when my friends became tired of thinking how else they might dispose of them. One volume I excavated – and one I read with complete and hungry attention, as if it were the greatest thriller ever written, through the first week of my stay in Woodhay – did, however, excite my particular interest. It was a book entitled *Clever Hans, The Horse of Mr Von Osten*, written by Oskar Pfungst and published in 1911. Clever Hans – or *Kluge Hans* in his original German – was a thoroughbred Orlov trotter dwelling in Berlin in the first decade of the twentieth century. This horse, owned by Wilhelm von Osten, a teacher of maths and a phrenologist – as well as a manifest lunatic, to judge by the play of his eyes – could count, add, subtract, multiply and divide, and could apply these functions in practical tests. It could also tell the time and differentiate musical notes, expressing all through the use of its right forehoof.

No longer compelled by some inner necessity to dive down into the depths of the ocean in my nightlong waking, nor finding my days requiring to be occupied with aimless thinkings, I woke each morning just like a normal person might, fetched my morning pastry from the step, went back to bed and read about the feats of this remarkable horse. It was not long before a growing weight of significance bore down on me from within whenever I considered the case of Clever Hans.

Already by 1905 or the year after, Hans had become famous for his prodigious talents, and was exhibited throughout Germany, appearing also in articles in newspapers across the world. The German Board of Education, hearing of this mysterious case, appointed philosopher and psychologist Carl Stumpf to establish a committee for the assessment of von Osten and his horse. It is only down to Stumpf's dedication to his science that the truth was revealed as to how Hans could achieve such feats of calculation and communication. But, in turn, the factual truths of Stumpf's conclusions were only a first step for me. Their further significance resonated in my mind long after I read the explanation. I would often catch myself having stood at the kitchen window or sat out in the garden on a low stool surrounded by precarious stacks of cracked pots for an hour or more, struggling to account for the vast profundity I felt in considering the implications of what Stumpf had discovered in regard to this horse. It was an inquiry which I will admit has never reached a satisfactory end. When my hosts returned from work in the evenings, I had such a tangle of signification knotted up inside of me that I couldn't even begin to speak about it.

The outcome of the committee's preliminary investigations – whose members included a vet, the director of a zoo and a circus manager – was that von Osten, contrary to the assumptions of senior members of the Board of Education, was not hoodwinking his audience: it was clear that there was no intention to deceive. Indeed, at the merest mention of trickery, von Osten would become violently angry, and could only be persuaded to calm down by the retraction of any possible suspicions as to his horse's genuine capabilities. Stumpf, astonished and perplexed, proceeded to test both human and horse, and after a series of trials discovered that Hans could count and calculate even if von Osten was not the person asking or presenting in writing the questions – even if, moreover, his master was not present at all. By long and careful experimentation, Stumpf went on to discover two prerequisites for the full demonstration of Hans' gift: first, that he be able to see the questioner; and second – and more intriguing and unexpected – that the questioner be aware of the answer to the question he or she were asking. Some of the committee could only conclude from this, though mostly in private, that Hans was an even greater miracle than they had thought – that there was no other explanation but that he must be capable of reading the minds of people. Little by little, however, it was revealed that Hans was engaging in neither rational thought nor telepathy, but rather was simply acting on the directions his interlocutor was relaying to him as plain as day. The truth was that, as Hans neared with the number of hoof taps the figure which would correctly answer the question he had been asked, the questioner who stood at his side grew increasingly tense with expectation. When the correct number was reached, the questioner's unconscious bodily responses to this climactic event – a release of tension, an opening of engagement, a great invitation to act, a 'Yes' of the spirit, urging the horse to get it right – led Hans to cease tapping, and so he reliably reached the number being demanded of him. Without knowing what that number was, the questioner would not exhibit such unconscious signs. Horses being such adept silent communicators – communicators one with another by the slightest movement – it was as obvious to Hans that he should cease tapping as it would be to a human being told, in a shout, 'STOP!' Stumpf, a methodical experimenter, tested this hypothesis from every angle to see if it could sustain the assault, and found that it was entirely sound. He discovered that even those people who knew they were being watched, and who knew of the way in which Hans was said to work, could not detect the infinitesimal movements they made in their own body, with their own head, in order to tell Hans when he should cease his tapping; nor could they stop themselves, try as they might, from giving him these messages. The only human participants who did not draw out the correct answers from the horse, other than those who did not know the answers to the questions they asked, were those who did not care. Perhaps, I reflected, desire performs some essential role in the communicative function. Perhaps it is a kind of demon in the machine which reverses the preternatural arrow of nature and creates order out of chaos, makes significance from meaninglessness. My back was warm against the weather-worn redbrick of the outhouse and the insects were in the air as I thought through the maze of it all. Von Osten, completely oblivious to these acts of communication he and his horse were engaged in, remained unconvinced by Stumpf's findings until his death, and great crowds, even though they were aware from the press coverage of the illusory nature of the demonstration, still came to see Hans answer questions correctly, and still they marvelled. 'My own view,' wrote Stumpf in a letter to his sister, 'is that it is a far greater and more affecting achievement for a horse to know what number you are thinking of from the way your body communicates unconsciously with it, than for him to be able to count and undertake simple mathematical problems.' Some years later, still on occasion led to reflect on the peculiar case of Clever Hans, Stumpf wrote again to his sister – who presumably had taken an interest in the matter, though none of her own correspondence survives – and made in a curious aside a comment which seems to be capable of bearing far more weight than it was originally built for: 'Von Osten was not deceiving his audience, his audience was deceiving itself.'

Through that first week of my stay, when my friends returned from work, we sat in the kitchen and talked for a while, prepared food, ate, and then played chess until we lost our patience with either the game or each other, whereupon we would head our separate ways to bed. It was a gentle and easy existence, for me at least. I heard them through the walls some nights talking, and though I could not make out any words, it was clear that there were difficulties, whether at work, financially, or between them. But perhaps I was imagining things – every voice, passing half-heard through the beams, plaster and horsehair of an old house, seems to sound out a lament.

It was on the day before my friends' departure for the Urals that I finished annotating Stumpf's book detailing the experiments made on Clever Hans. I flicked back through the pages, observing how my handwritten notes, which engulfed the text of some pages while leaving others entirely immaculate, denoted where the storms of my interest had taken place. Placing the book on my bedside table, I went downstairs to feed myself, and could not help reflecting that, if Linda Wouters can pick up a man's finger while it is still attached to him and type messages on his behalf, while all the time believing – and the doctors and journalists all around her believe also – that the voice coming out of the end of that finger is Rom Houben's; if Hans the horse can stand beside a man or woman, be asked a question, respond accurately to it, and his audience perceive him – notwithstanding their complete knowledge of the means by which he succeeds in such a feat – to be an extraordinary example of his species, endowed with special gifts that lift him almost out of that species into theirs, the most exalted species which has ever existed on earth, the work of a vanishingly improbable chance of evolutionary development; if humans have this ability to deceive themselves in a great chain of wish-fulfilment, one upon another, out of the strength of their desire; is it then in fact so surprising that an entire nation can discover a group among them – one which had been numbered among their own, to have lived in their streets, and shopped at their shops – and set about systematically murdering it, all the time being oblivious to this act's wrongness, without knowing that they in fact were doing this? And, if all of these, then how much easier it is to picture a person, doused in loneliness, conceiving himself of a secret love communicated to him by coded messages, and all the numerous outcomes which this might entail, even his own death. Delusions are delusions only because they are aberrations from an accepted account of the world; if it's a delusion we all agree on, and nobody notices, what then? I suppose we call that culture, or reality, whether it's the assertion of a new meaning to a word or an act of mass murder.

★

One day last autumn my father came to visit and brought with him two panniers filled with the last of Mark's possessions. My first instinct was that I must update my list of his things – perhaps this would make looking at them bearable. Within were numerous books of mathematics, a volume containing the lyrics to every song Bob Dylan ever wrote, several popular science books examining consciousness and neuroscience, and a chessboard. After my father left, I emptied both panniers out on to the floor but found no pieces to go with this last item. Can one play chess without the pieces? Which is more important, these or the board? I felt a strange sensation that terrestrial life is a chessboard and we are the figures. (Which, in particular, then, are we?)

In one of the very few photographs he allowed to be taken of him, my brother sits beside Paolozzi's Newton statue at the British Library, curiously echoing, in variation, that giant's pose, though playing chess instead of making a circle with compasses: legs crossed, elbow folded, hand crooked across his thinking mouth – he appears to be some manner of chess-playing machine which has been folded into its correct shape for working, perhaps by the metal god looming above. Living in Nottingham, he survived on a tin of tomatoes every few days, perhaps the occasional egg, bingeing on pasties whenever it happened that he clawed a little money together. He wrote equations which look beautiful and mean nothing to almost everyone. He played chess all night. One of his two or three regular opponents was a fellow mathematician, a gentle and serious young man whose name I cannot recall, but whom I met only once, at a memorial gathering six months or so after Mark's death. This gentle and serious man who I did not know in the slightest spoke movingly about my brother, and it was a comfort to know that it was still possible to like him. Inside one of the panniers there was a wedding invitation which, with a leap of excitement I thought for an instance was to this gentle and serious man's wedding, but it was not. Nevertheless, this was sufficient to recall to me the time when this man did marry and asked Mark to be his best man – the very idea of it makes me wince: responsibility. This pleasant, clean and polite young groom might as well have asked a Baudelaire or a bear. He soon discovered – though surely he knew already – that he would be compelled by the condition of Mark's clothes to buy him a suit and shoes for the event. This he did, and when it came to the special day, Mark of course could not be found. He had simply disappeared, along with the ring too. No one knows where he had gone or what he was doing, but it was predictable enough.

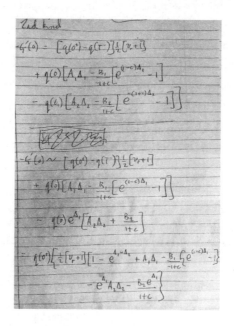

When I think back to the multitude of catastrophes which he left in a trail behind him, I smile. It takes a lot of strength and courage to invent the day, every single day, out of nothing; to ride chaos like it were a saddleless horse. The most incredible thing about those sheets of paper covered in his equations is their neatness, so at odds with his way of living in every other respect. And I did not know that the shape of one's handwriting can carry the character of the writer as fully in numbers as it can in writing. Here, under the forms of impenetrable equations, is the very character of my brother.

*

At the end of the week, on the last day of the summer term – as well as my friends' last in their house before they left for six weeks (how I longed for their departure) – we ate out. The teachers were now willing to take some risks with their drinking, the talk turned silly, and so, when we got back to the house, a large sheet of heavy paper was obtained, and we attempted to draught a chessboard we had theorised in the pub upon which three players could compete on equal terms with each other. The squares would be hexagons; these hexagons would be black, white and red; and forward movements of pieces could be in two directions, towards either opponent. However, our excitement as we worked very soon turned to confusion when we attempted to colour the hexagons such that moves could be made in a logically coherent way, straight across the three colours alternating in turn, and diagonal along identical colours. No matter how we arranged it, nothing could be made to work; patterns confidently begun set up internal conflicts with themselves by the time the second or third row was attempted. Diagonal moves required so much calculation, and resembled straight lines so little, that no one dared to attempt them. Anticipating even a single move in advance of both opponents involved so many possibilities of such peculiarity of movement that within a short space of time everyone had forgotten what they were attempting to achieve, and on at least one occasion even who they were. The only figure which seemed suited to this disfigured iteration of chess was the horse, which pleased me a great deal, since I had become on such a close footing with the creatures in the past week. Every other piece quickly stumbled and fell, while the horse surged on, or round, ploughing up little sickle shapes across the board, deft and delicate and directionless, a constant source of surprise, like the crescents of light made in the surface of a fast-moving river by the sunlight.

That night I dreamed I was not wholly myself, but half you, perhaps fully both of us; and I – we – played chess, except not between ourselves or self, but against the horse Hans, after all three of our deaths. In real life – whatever that might mean – Hans became property of the state after his master Von Osten died, and was exhibited for a short while before being co-opted into the war effort, where all trace of him is lost. I like to imagine that he eyed that battlefield out there before him, and, in between the lines of his own men and the enemy, there was his own way, his hooked and fugitive approach to things, which eschewed the lines of aims and targets, of a battle held straight on, perpendicular to the defensive lines of the men beneath him in the trenches, but rather followed a horseful logic, one in which much can be achieved simply by standing still in a field somewhere, as horses do.

And when I woke up, my friends were gone, and the house had altered in feeling: its insides like an echo of the insides of me.

★

Between bouts of reading, through all the long days sitting with my ankle raised on a cushion in front of me, my thoughts wandering wherever they might go, I tended always to return by some route or other to the figure of Clever Hans the horse. Still I was unable to discover the precise significance this story held for me, but I felt a strong and certain truthfulness in it which refused to dissipate with time. This interest in Hans the horse eventually branched out and led me by a lurching, fragmented, grotesque taxonomy through the shape of my own broken thoughts. The horse – horses in general – though they had never interested me in the slightest before, began to assume a monumental importance. They promised to solve some obscure riddle of existence which I had never before considered. I undertook researches into horses in war, horses in chess, horses as workers, horses as signs and emblems, horses as vehicles. I tried to think myself into the places and minds of those people who first domesticated the horse on the steppe eight thousand years ago and more and then rode out across Europe to make what would become everything around me. It is true and astonishing that a single language swarmed down on the backs of horses from the Caspian steppe across the continent and conquered every tongue from the Norwegian Sea to the Bay of Bengal, from Kazakhstan to the west of Ireland. From a narrow point of time and place, to this: hundreds of languages across a quarter of the globe. Am I right to say that this is another instantiation of entropy, that all systems, even the linguistic, move from order towards disorder? Or perhaps, with language, it's the opposite, because the tongue is lazy. He – you – would know. All these hundreds of thousands of words and meanings, threads which make up the fabric of the hundreds of daughter languages, exhibiting the utmost subtlety and sophistication, brought into such combinations as can make the hair stand up on the back of your neck and your mind rush with an apprehension of the vertiginous power of a simple idea or image perfectly stated. And yet it is nothing other than an illusion: a gaggle of sounds formed by some flaps held inside a mucous membrane. There is no bullion in the vaults of the bank of meaning, just an endless supply of slips of paper and a hollow blowing of wind. And once they are blown, there is no retrieving them.

And if I did all this sitting and reading and thinking in order to draw further away from the fact of you – of him – then I drew closer at once; and if I did it in order to trim down towards an originary moment, a unitary explication, so that the time would be healed, then all that I discovered was more and more: replications, multitudinous echoes from multifarious sources.

★

When my ankle had healed enough to tolerate the riding of a bicycle, I spent several hours each day rushing down the canopied lanes and along the broad edges of the cornfields between Newbury, Andover and Marlborough, and remembering how I had done the same from village to village in North Essex when I was young – Pebmarsh, Lamarsh, Alphamstone – and newly discovering the freedom of movement which growing older and owning a bicycle allowed. I do not know what it was my friends had seen in me that day after I had opened the door and allowed them to invite me across the country to their house, but certainly I was unaware that all was not well with the mind and the body that I suppose I must call myself.

Perhaps it was a sign of improvement – whatever that might mean – that I developed a daily routine. I took my breakfast whenever I woke, and read in bed until mid-morning. Following this, I walked across the fields up to Pilot Hill, the highest point in Hampshire; or else cycled in an improvised loop through the Downs. Either way, I returned to the house for a late lunch, and proceeded to read where I had left off for an hour or two. Concluding this, and in spite of the directive that I should not feel obliged to perform any chores, I would go round the house and address the multiple minor repairs which had overwhelmed my friends, or else take the axe out of the store and head out to the shed to chop wood, a completely unnecessary undertaking, owing to it being only the beginning of August, but a satisfying one nevertheless.

★

One morning, I cycled out north towards Swindon through the village of Kintbury and then Hungerford, passing under the limbs of the twisted grey oaks which lined the road and sometimes encroached on its edge, pushing it into an elbow as a toppled rock does a stream. At Eddington, I came down to the banks of the Kennet and turned west, determining to follow its course. For several miles I departed from and then returned to its side as the road saw fit, a brisk tail wind making light work of the shallow ascent up the valley. Just the other side of Ramsbury, where White's Hill begins to climb up out of the Kennet valley over the Marlborough Downs in long and tentative search of the Thames, I stopped at a field's edge to eat an apple, whereupon a mare and her foal, seeing me from the other side, came trotting over. This pleased me a great deal. When a cat comes to you, it will lean into your touch; when a dog, it will respond to your movement and fit into the world with you in a negotiation of played space. A horse does neither of these, but comes – sometimes at a trot, sometimes at a low and lazy walk – and stops walking when it has reached its destination, which is you. It does not seem to care whether it is fondled or not, but stands before you in a most peculiar grace. There is something autistically human about a horse, which comes too close, says nothing, and appears to wait without letting you know what for. These two which had come to do just this at me now stood with their heads over the wire fence, unmoving except for little ticking turns to the head to ward off the flies and the occasional spasm to the flank. They faced me as if waiting for the thing I had said would happen to happen. Didn't they know that I hadn't said anything? It may have been that my knowledge of horses had increased in the preceding month. However, now, as I stood there with my apple and these two before me, I found that I had only theoretical knowledge of this species. It is true that I could now name and point out many of the parts of these horses – withers, stifle, croup, gaskin, pastern, coronet, fetlock – but it took a great reserve of courage for me to reach up and offer a hand out for the touching of a nose. And in fact, as if in proof of this, I moved too quickly, and both horses shied away from me obliquely, as if a mooring had slipped loose and they had been forced away from me by a hidden current. They turned fully away, trotted up and over a bluff, and the foal began to play, nudging its mother at the shoulder and shaking its nose in that way a human infant has of proudly refusing food.

I thought then of how my brother for many years – or it seemed so to me as a child – refused to eat anything except peanut butter on toast. His face was rosy at the cheeks with teething and greasy about the mouth with the remnants of whichever meal he had taken; hard to tell, because breakfast, lunch and dinner were for him identical. And I felt the urge to present the facts of the case, even though facts are only the skeleton – if that. Perhaps the facts are, in fact, nothing but a convenient image we can share with each other, one liable to obscure truth, just as a photograph destroys real memories and creates false; or like a definition in the dictionary, entirely lacking the connotative function of language, the feelings a word provokes, which is surely its true heart.

★

If, in the course of a conversation with someone I do not know very well the topic seems to be drifting toward that dangerous question which can be said in so many ways – 'So tell me, do you have a sibling?', 'How many brothers or sisters do you have?', 'Where did you grow up?', 'Don't you have a brother?', 'What's his name again?', 'How's Mark?' – I marshal great expeditious cunning and divert the talk into a less dangerous channel, or else I pretend not to have heard. It is far less work not to bother talking to people at all.

This does not mean I don't feel a pressure to speak.

It is just that I prefer to have no audience.

And I'd prefer to have no words – words do present a significant problem.

Yes, I want to speak the unspeakable – to talk about what it is forbidden to talk about. I do not mean by the culture around me, which asserts very often that it very much wants me to talk (though I suspect that really it does not). Speaking it is forbidden myself by myself because it is not made of words, and so how can I? Everything which is written here is trimming, preparation, circling, awaiting. Something must burst through in truth or it will remain unspeakable.

Until such time – or, in the absence of this – I'm going to give an account of what happened.

My brother phoned me one day to say that our father had threatened him with a knife. He had been staying with him for several months after an abrupt move away from a little house perched high above the long wind-stretched sands of the Gower Peninsula. The suddenness of that move is another story, but it is worth recording that each story of sudden upheaval leads back to another which precedes it until, if we followed this concatenation of disasters back in recession through all the spots of dislocated time to its origin, what would be found? It is tempting to imagine a first cause, but it is a delusion as serious and erroneous as the one which ate him up. Whether true or not (the accusation of threat by knife was improbable), relations between my brother and father were, as they had always tended to be, not good. And so I invited Mark to stay with me.

A series of buses and trains must have brought him from Clare, where he was staying with our father, on the Suffolk–Essex border, up to Norwich, because certainly I did not go to collect him. Each night he made up a bed in the front room, which in the day he didn't really clear away, and he left a small crumpled pile of clothing perpetually beside it, the smell from which permeated the air and filled each room, the strength diminishing with distance from source, like the power of an empire as it decreases across a continent, though still felt nevertheless at its farthest edge. The last time he had stayed I was writing up my thesis about David Jones' great poem *The Anathemata*, and he remarked one night after I described Jones' manuscript and the method of its writing that the process and its resultant structure brought to mind – his, at least – the geometrical figure of the fractal. He explained to me that in the fractal a primary form or shape is repeated at every scale of its being from the very pop into origin at the instance of its first calculation, its genesis, up to its theoretically infinite expanse, for a fractal feeds its product back into itself continually forever. These iterative structures, he continued, are found in nature – for example in a fern's stem supporting multiple leaves, each of which supports multiple miniature leaves just like itself, and so on; or in romanesco, which appears as a kind of digital broccoli, with swirls replicated, if you look closely, down below the scale one can see, and up through every swirl which forms another with its neighbours, up to whole heads of vorticularly internested twists and twirls, selves within selves at every scale, and each of these heads going on to form with its neighbours a whole which is no different. This being the case, he went on, then why should such structures not be found in a product of the human mind, which must at its most fundamental level have a simple means of indication, nothing more than a switch (YES/NO, I/O, ON/OFF). And this being at the origin or base of growth, then what is at the top is bound to be the same. And if the evidence of language and the thereby visible desire for humans to understand by opposition is anything to go by, everything, structurally speaking, is the same, a great complexity built out of the simplest of base functions in reiteration.

Which I suppose would account for the great repetitious mess of history.

This summary of the ways of fractal geometry led me to a month's research and writing, which in turn formed the conclusion of my thesis. Accordingly, I wrote in the acknowledgements page of my thesis that I was indebted to my brother for this analogy. Several years later he made the accusation that he had written the whole thesis and that I had stolen it from him, and that my PhD was nothing but a brazen feat of plagiarism.

But I am not intending to settle scores.

My brother arrived in Norwich, and maybe he surprised me by being upbeat from the very beginning, but I cannot remember. Certainly, within a few weeks he was excited by something, and it did not take many pints in the Alexandra Tavern at the end of the road to discover that the source of this excitement was Lou, though he maintained a cryptic purview of their relations for me. He asked to use my computer often, and concealed the details of this usage from me. If I walked into my bedroom – this was where I had my laptop set up, on an ancient little table with cast-iron wheels which cried out as if in grief whenever it was moved – my brother would turn the desk and thereby also the open laptop, rotating it out of my sight, and in curious counterpoint turn his own face the opposite way to look up at me in this way he had with it that made clear my presence in the room, my own bedroom, was an imposition sufficient to cause real and actual offence.

But really I am not intending to settle scores here – or not entirely.

About our father he repeated the phrase 'It's beyond the pale.' In regard to Lou he spent long days and night on the computer and dwelt there in childlike excitement and secrecy. Within or beside the malodorous pile of clothes bunched up in the front room he left several disposable safety razors which, in an attempt to tidy up, I cut my fingers on, though this was not the reason why, in the end, after six weeks, I told him he wasn't welcome any longer.

Midway through his six-week stay, one which ended as abruptly and unexpectedly as all the other endings (perhaps the only ending he made which was not abrupt or unexpected is that of his own life, for I had been forewarned, given the chance to confess, and so on), I travelled from Norwich to Walthamstow to visit a friend. Earlier that week, she (her name is Claire) had posted the comment 'Are you losing your mind?!' in response to a sequence of several dozen comments made by my brother in response to a photograph of two young rabbits he had posted on Lou's Facebook wall. I had liked the thread because the comments were enthusiastic and amusing ('Look at the two of them,' etc.), which was something my brother now rarely was.

In the morning we drove east across Essex to a mutual friend's wedding, for which we were compelled to dress in medieval clothes. As a monk, I spoke little and drank much, though when I noticed long after the ceremony late in the afternoon that Lou, dressed as a princess, was at the wedding too – for she had grown up in the same town as us – I crossed the lawn in order to tease her about the association she was developing with my brother, and for the rabbits.

We humans are ordinarily capable of overturning an enormous complex of knowledge and belief we have built up over weeks or months, to understand in an instant that everything is not how we had imagined (where we are incapable of such a thing, we are categorised as 'delusional'); this, as she turned to me, before she even spoke, was one of those moments. I did not need her to speak. In fact, I cannot remember if she spoke at all. Perhaps she said, Tell him to stay away from me. Or, Nothing's happening. Or perhaps she just shook her head and walked away. The last of these possibilities feels most right. Certainly, apart from sensing disaster in the form her face had taken – it was clear that no further information was required – I did not acquire any definite information, and so I sought out Mati, who had remained a loyal friend to Mark through nearly twenty years of strange and often inappropriate behaviour.

We'll talk about it tomorrow, she said.

I write now that this tomorrow's conversation never happened, and I reason with myself that I must have left early, or Mati did, or the hangover forbade discussion of serious matters, because it feels correct. It is not only that I cannot remember having this conversation; there is a *feeling* that I can't have. Why? One possible interpretation of this is that the memory is already being converted into myth, and one in accordance with outcomes which were unguessable at that time: I am aestheticising an element of the story so that it comports with the tragic rather than comic. Or my memory, structured by feeling, prepares certain paradigms to play out the tragic story.

If I am honest with myself – but of course I cannot be honest with myself. I cannot see because two worlds collide. I preclude the truth of facts from myself because there is a bigger truth of feeling, which motivates the construction of myth, which is memory told as story. In my telling, I must return home without knowledge of the difference between Mark's illusion and Lou's reality, so that it is unmediated. I must see it unravelling: I must enter the abandoned house alone at night because this is how we have always come to understand terror.

In short, when I arrived home, I can't have known nothing, but memory is the servant of feeling, and so I knew nothing.

*

The primary cause of Mark's death was in all probability loneliness, but not directly. Suicide became his only conceivable solution to the exhausting problem of a manic enthusiasm for pernicious delusional conspiracy on the one hand and the blankness of a life under the soporific of antipsychotic medication on the other. But the conspiracy mania had its source in an infatuation with Lou, an infatuation which had at its heart a longing to be no longer alone, exiled, too much in this separated and singular body, apart. On the web page of the Cleveland Clinic, which deals with delusional disorder, the causes of this condition are said to be unknown, but of the environmental and psychological causes evidence points to stress, drugs and alcohol, and isolation – immigrants and people with sight or hearing defects exhibit higher morbidity rates. The worst thing that there can be is to live without love. Under the pressure of these delusions, Mark lost the opportunity to receive love; under the fog of his medication, he lost the capacity to give or feel it. One can be spurned and exiled and still survive if one can continue to feel a love for what is in our proximity, or even what is beyond. As long as there is love.

When I challenged Mark about his behaviour with Lou – for it had become clear that he was harassing her – he admitted after a while that she had been sending secret messages to him expressing her devotion, and he had now learned to understand them all perfectly, though they seemed strange, and no, he didn't expect me to believe in any of it. He went no further than this. The mass of evidence he had for her love was as large as the mass of evidence he later had for the conspiracy we were all waging against him. I learned from Mati of a photograph taken in Malaysia of Lou standing beside a statue of a monkey with the comment 'My monkey boyfriend' which had been posted on Facebook at least a year before Mark was even reminded of her existence and began his interest, a photograph which was later interpreted by him as being a secret message of love. The network of connections Mark made between the individual words and phrases of her messages and his own, sometimes forming a stitching which ran between great numbers of them of incredible intricacy, was preposterous from the outside. His long string of messages on her Facebook page in response to his own picture of two leverets was not, as it appeared, a sequence of charming if unorthodox flirtations: he was quoting earlier messages she herself had posted on Facebook over the previous few years in order to let her know that he understood, and that he felt the same way. Lou overturned my illusions about Mark's own illusions at the wedding with a single look because he had already travelled to London to meet her several weeks before, where they had had a very awkward meeting during which he believed himself to be finally making himself available to her after she had been secretly pursuing him for so long. As far as Lou was aware, she was meeting an old half-friend for a drink, with perhaps the possibility that something might happen in the future. And of course something did. The moment I discovered the intricate arabesques of the sign world which entwined my brother and Lou in his imagination felt like that moment in a horror film when the girl realises it is in the house with her.

I sometimes wonder how long this primordial, inanimate soup lay in his mind waiting for the spark that would bring about its origin of life.

We are more similar than you think, Mark said to me that time. This is not true, not because we are not similar, but because I do in fact recognise the similarity. If I drink too much, the next day I am distorted by the influx of a demonic presence into every element and thread of myself. This malevolent presence occupies every plane of existence: material, spiritual, ideational, emotional, and so on. In fact, it negates all these realities, and discovers for me that there is nothing, that my thoughts, feelings and sensations are no more than chemical mutterings, like the movement of bacteria within a Petri dish. My brother, when he drinks too much – when he drank – experienced much the same, except it wasn't horror or anxiety which pursued him and leeched all the goodness and reality out of his world, but a desperation to be elsewhere, or maybe to be nowhere. All his many odysseys across the country from one friend's sofa to another were transacted or at least begun under the aegis of nothing more than a powerful hangover. Stability would only return after several days, by which time it was often too late – the job, or flat, or partner was no longer his. When Mark returned to Norwich after his drinking bout in London, and the subsequent attempt to meet Lou, he sent her over forty desperate text messages. These began with the assertion that he was coming to find her in Hampstead and ended with God knows what.

What happened next is very interesting. Mark's analysis of what had taken place between himself and Lou had to alter, because Lou's treatment of him after he had met her on their date and informed her that he knew of her love contrasted so starkly with the expressions of that love which had been made formerly. And yet the most obvious and simple alteration, the most obvious and simple solution – to admit that he had misinterpreted the secret messages, that there hadn't been any messages at all – was entirely impossible to reach. In the same way as mathematics is an intricate logical and coherent system within itself, while being utterly meaningless if its foundations are undermined, or if its foundational premises are not grasped (cats, for example, hold no truck for numbers, while at the same time being expert in the calculation of the parabola of the landing sparrow, probabilities in regard to the routes of mice, and other points of existence in which we humans have discovered complex mathematical functions at work), so Mark's desire for coherence and logic – he had been studying dynamical systems and advanced mathematics for several years before this – led him to the formulation of a modified conclusion which was utterly incoherent and improbable to anyone else: Lou had posted all the secret messages on Facebook in order to *pretend* to love him, so that she could torment and humiliate him after he capitulated to her feigned desires and was ensnared by his own genuine ones. For Mark, this was the only credible explanation. In other words, for the lonely, it is better to be hated and humiliated than ignored, because at least it proves one's existence.

From here onward there were arrests, cautions, a conviction (I do not even know for what. Harassment, probably). There were restraining orders which were broken. Never did he make explicit threat of violence, but as one of the many recipients of his cryptic messages, violence felt likely, despite his normally non-violent temperament. It is only now, eight or so years on from this, and four years on from his death (time keeps turning: now, as I edit this, it is about to become five, six, seven), that I discover in the conclusion of the previous sentence that it must have required enormous resourcefulness and abnegation of will for my brother to resist the urge to violence when everyone who had meant anything to him was trying to destroy him.

There are always two ways of looking at anything.

★

I know that you hung on the windy tree, wounded with a Kitchen Devil, dedicated to nothing much, yourself to yourbitterself, on that tree and no other, at that specific point, ordinals temporal and spatial, and opened up a little keyhole of oblivion in the bright Suffolk springtime, where the time drained through. What I or anyone else is to do about this fact is the greatest mystery, akin to looking in the dark at some disturbance of the sight, and finding that the more directly and intently we peer at anything, the less visible it becomes.

★

There is a highly entertaining passage in Rousseau's *Confessions* in which the author, at the age of twenty, having become lost on the return journey from a commission to deliver a friend to her father, arrives in Lausanne and finds himself once again away from home without money, friend or opportunity. This, for much of the peculiar Genevan's youth, constituted a kind of method for living. On this occasion, having recently met and fallen into an infatuation with a rakish though highly skilled musician who dubbed himself Venture de Villeneuve (the philosopher was prone to a quick love), he conceived an image of himself in replication of this maestro as a music teacher and composer named, anagrammatically of his own if we allow a 'v' to become a 'u' as it once first did, Vaussore, also a de Villeneuve from Paris. After acquiring credit from a M. Perrotet for lodgings at his house and a number of young students from around the town, Rousseau soon thereafter met a professor of Law and amateur music lover called M. de Treytorens, and found himself volunteering for a commission to produce a piece of music for a concert organised by this gentleman; a piece Rousseau, or perhaps more accurately

Vaussore, wrote with very great enthusiasm and dedication, though neither skill nor knowledge. It does seem a difficult thing to be two people at once; being only one is hard enough. The night of the concert arrived; Rousseau took the conductor's baton, readied himself and counted the orchestra in. The effect upon the ear, so the composer recalls, was appalling, and both Vaussore and Rousseau had to carry the humiliation of two people within one body for the duration of the concert and for a long time after.

The following day, after confessing in tears his deception to a member of the orchestra, Vaussore was found to have become missing, for Rousseau's secret became known the whole town round, and Rousseau was Rousseau, which was to say nobody, though no one in the town out of kindness would admit that they knew the two had been the same.

Not long after this humiliation, Rousseau began walking the Canton de Vaud down to the village of Vevey for a consolation, and discovered there a landscape which affected him with such extremes of emotion that he would often sit down on a bluff or rock and weep in his luscious melancholy. 'I cannot live without an orchard on the shores of that lake, and no other,' he wrote of Lac Léman, which curls from Geneva at its south-western tip up past Lausanne on its northern shore to Montreux in the east. 'I must have a constant friend, a charming wife, a cow, and a little boat. I shall not enjoy perfect happiness on earth until I have all these.' On Sundays, if it did not rain, Rousseau walked north from Lausanne up the valley along the road, now carrying the denomination Route 5, for six miles to reach his nearest Catholic church, a walk he often shared with a fellow Catholic. Rousseau, an inveterate fabricator, continued to claim himself to be from Paris, and found in this companion a confederate, perhaps an awkward discovery for one who had never himself been to that city despite his assertion of origins there. Fortunately for the nascent philosopher, though, this man enjoyed talking about Paris so much that he refused to suspect Rousseau of deceiving him, even though, as Rousseau himself wrote, 'this gentleman was not a Parisian of my sort, but a true Parisian from Paris.'

How is it that Jean-Jacques Rousseau can be dead? It does not seem possible that such a vivid and lively voice can be lost. In his adolescence he discovered what every adolescent must begin to discover for him- and herself: that the world is relatively indifferent to us. Fortunately, the adolescent is given at the same time the opportunity to discover a source of comfort in oneself in the form of the hand and what it can do in regard to the genitals below. Rousseau wanked like a caged bear in comfort of himself from the moment he discovered his great gift. At about the same age, two hundred and seventy years later, one could walk into my brother's room at any time of the day and note his position in the bed – he refused to go to school – and the presence of a wastepaper basket overflowing with encrusted tissues. Both men in later life, who had been so similar in their mendicant and emotional youths, wandering from town to town without purpose or plan, who dreamed of regions beyond sense and sensation, pure intellectual realms, became overwhelmed by delusional paranoia. Perhaps compulsive masturbation is a sign of moral corruption after all, as the Victorians declared. Or perhaps we are all in danger of being swallowed into the cave of ourselves, where meaning both emanates and ends, and we must find comfort where we can.

Reader, you do it too.

Masturbation, I discovered, has occupied a more elevated place in some cultures and times than the grotty fold of flesh we find it in today. In ancient Heliopolis, now buried beneath the Ein Shams suburb of Cairo, the creation of the universe out of an elemental potential was attributed to Atum, whose name is said to mean also 'finisher'. He came before, and he will come after. Atum, they say, achieved this miracle of creation *ex nihilo* in imitation of his own self-creation, which itself was conceptualised and symbolised by the image of masturbation, a be-coming. He is everything which is against sense and the intelligible, but which must in some way have been and is: he is in union with his own shadow, he is male and female, he dies and births himself, he is the day and the night, self-renewing with every rotation of the earth. That first discovery of orgasm is life and death wrapped in one little package of self-discovery, the big hit, a stepping beyond the limits of matter and time. This kind of paradoxical explanation is in no way inimical to science. Paradox used to be the highest form of sense and significance, and indeed now, with the growth in the popular imagination of quantum mechanics, appears to be coming back to take a place in accepted forms of scientific discourse. What is impossible is, in a sense, what must be, *because* it is impossible. If it were possible, it would not explain, because explanation nullifies, has limits, borders, systemic edges beyond which – what? In order to have no walls, we must have mystery, paradox, impossibility.

Paradox and impossibility stand most necessarily at the origins of things. How can something – proteins, horses, chess, slavery – just become? The origin and development of language is one such conundrum. August Schleicher was the first of the great nineteenth-century German philologists to formulate the image of the family tree in a theorisation of the development of languages. To Schleicher, a language was as much a living thing as a fern or gorilla. Taking Darwin's discoveries in biology as confirmation of his suspicions, Schleicher saw that the languages of Europe were growing more complex but also less numerous. In contradiction of the prevailing theories of his time, he proposed and proved with reference to an enormous quantity of linguistic data gathered by himself and his predecessors that the languages of Europe had in the distant past been much more numerous, and that the idea of an originary language was a myth. From where, though, did these multiple antecedent languages come? Ever more languages? Were they more youthful, or are we led to such conceptions by our inability to see beyond three generations into the past? In truth, the family tree tapers inwards and outwards both up and down, from single points and whole generations, outward and inward from ourselves and all who seem to have been necessary in our generation, and all who sweep past us without suspecting a mote of our individual existence in the darkness of time. Languages stemmed from more languages, but where did they come from? The seductive pull of the idea of a singular origin – the desire for a sense which feels right and good – always, however, wins. Schleicher, working against his own principles, traced the languages of Europe back to a Proto-Indo-European root, albeit a reconstructed and theoretical one, and in 1868 wrote and published the first piece of writing in that language. This, a parable about a sheep taking advice from horses, goes like this:

Avis, jasmin varnā na ā ast, dadarka akvams, tam, vāgham garum vaghantam, tam, bhāram magham, tam, manum āku bharantam. Avis akvabhjams ā vavakat: kard aghnutai mai vidanti manum akvams agantam. Akvāsas ā vavakant: krudhi avai, kard aghnutai vividvant-svas: manus patis varnām avisāms karnauti svabhjam gharmam vastram avibhjams ka varnā na asti. Tat kukruvants avis agram ā bhugat.

[On a hill,] a sheep that had no wool saw horses, one of them pulling a heavy wagon, one carrying a big load, and one carrying a man quickly. The sheep said to the horses: 'My heart pains me, seeing a man driving horses.' The horses said: 'Listen, sheep, our hearts pain us when we see this: a man, the master, makes the wool of the sheep into a warm garment for himself. And the sheep has no wool.' Having heard this, the sheep fled into the plain.

There is something touching to the consideration of this Thuringian linguist sitting within his little study at home in the woods piecing together a language out of all the shards contained in those which survive it – English, German, French, Danish, Spanish, Italian, Romanian, and so on – in order to what? He believed that languages were like – and even at times in his writing can be interpreted as saying that they *were* – living beings. They have life cycles: youth, maturity, death. But their beginnings and their ends are non-existent. 'To assume one original universal language is impossible; there are rather many original languages: this is a certain result obtained by the comparative treatment of the languages of the world which have lived till now. Since languages are continually dying out, whilst no new ones practically arise, there must have been originally many more languages than at present. The number of original languages was therefore certainly far larger than has been supposed from the still-existing languages.' The fact of the non-death of this ancient language which Schleicher reconstructed in a simple fable is intrinsic to that reconstruction: it still survives in the words which half of the world's population speak today, the grammar which carries those words, and which continues to organise our thought, and yet it never existed. These things, almost entirely obscured, sinking back into nothing, soon to be lost but here still – poignancy, we find, is capable of soaking into the fibres even of the rawest data.

★

Aristotle tells of a stallion which, discovering it had mated with its mother, took itself to a clifftop and leapt to its death. This could

145

not but make me recall one of the etchings made by William Blake in the 1790s for his *Marriage of Heaven and Hell*, in which two horses fall headlong into hell surrounded by flames. In the same poem Blake writes of his own craft as etcher as if it were some alchemical process, where varnish is applied with a brush to copper plates and acid used to eat away at the bare metal to reveal the intended illustration, the infinite which was hid, as he puts it. People have this compulsion to take one thing and make it into another. What is the purpose of this, this desire to make signification, that which it is said makes us human? In my researches I stumbled upon a story of a Newfoundland dog, published in the 'Country News' section of the *Illustrated London News* in April 1845, which had taken its own life in the brisk blackflowing waters of the Ribble, just before it meets the Holme:

Singular case of suicide by a dog — On Saturday last, a fine, hand-some, and valuable black dog, of the Newfoundland species, belonging to Mr Floyd, solicitor, Holmfirth, Yorkshire committed suicide by drowning itself in the river which flows at the back of the owner's habitation. For some days previous the animal seemed less animated than usual, but on this particular occasion he was noticed to throw himself into the water and endeavour to sink by preserving perfect stillness of the legs and feet. Being dragged out of the stream, the dog was tied up for a time, but had no sooner been released than he again hastened to the water and again tried to sink and was again got out. This occurred many times, until at length the animal with repeated efforts appeared to get exhausted, and by dint of keeping his head determinedly under water for a few minutes, succeeded at last in obtaining his object, for when taken out this time he was indeed dead. The case is worth recording, as affording another proof of the general instinct and sagacity of the canine race.

Although animal psychologists, I discovered with a little further digging, now maintain unanimously that no action of an animal can ever lead us to describe its death as suicide, there stands in the village of Milton in West Dunbartonshire a bridge from which, since the mid 1950s, close to a thousand dogs have leapt. Of these, over fifty have died. In every case, the dogs have jumped from the same spot between two piers of the Overtoun Bridge. They have all been long-nosed breeds and the day has always been clear and bright. Soon after discovering this, I read of the events of only a few years ago in Switzerland, two hours' drive from Rousseau's lake, in the village of Lauterbrunnen in the Alps, in which twenty-eight cows and bulls ran without explanation over the edge of a cliff to their deaths in three days. These days, as I ride this old creaking bike along the lanes of the Sussex Downs, I see the livestock speckle the hills and the preoccupations of my imagination, the unrelieved pressure of my preoccupations, makes it impossible not to play with their tiny forms and thrust them like a motley of chess pieces across the hills towards a communal disaster which my mind hasn't fully prepared for them yet. When the imagination does something like this, I understand that it is exercising itself on the raw material of its consciousness, but isn't it peculiar how if it urges these cattle across the hills, herding them at speed towards their death, this motion is always starting up, never unfolding or progressing, but ever at play between a before and after, motion without moving, pure desire. It would be very easy to be drawn into this pool, to be sucked down into this pool of signs, where there is desire and imagination and no check on the interplay between the two, until all sense of the four-sides-square of words is lost and the magical kernel is perceived to be known in all its mysteries, which of course is insanity. The mind would then be lost to time, and the body shiver in a little room for decades waiting for its expiration, though the moments, days and years revolve around and around within the mechanism of everlasting time. Here, matter can be made so cold that time is brought to stop.

★

My brother had drowned in a tide of over-significance, one in which everything became coded, and all to a single purpose. Perhaps that is it, that we humans, in order to remain sane, must remain open to the scatteredness of signification, its Brownian motion, the unpredictability of its movement, the *probabilistic* nature of communication between people, even though this feels itself like an abyss. Speaking for myself, there was discernible everywhere around me, in every source of information, through all of these many old equestrian books which for some reason I found myself drawn to read, the very real possibility of a shearing-off. Yes, the words would still *mean*, but to what value and in what currency? Wherever there is a word, there is a weight.

For a long time now I have sought to become aware of the specific shape to the significance of these things which have come to mean so much to me, Clever Hans being no different from the others in this respect. And yet isn't the indefiniteness of that shape a part of its very significance? To pin Hans down is an assault on him, indelicate, distasteful, vulgar. It is enough that he and the many others have entered that circle of what is loved and known which dwells at the centre of our selves. And those most capable of making that crossing – from the realm of matter, ephemera, the everyday, into eternity – are always those things which do not answer but only ask. A knock of the hoof three times – this is no mathematical product but rather an inquisition into the solidity of the very earth. It will be found to be entirely devoid of substance when the time piles up and pushes us down.

★

Taking a break from my equine interest for a book or two, I was leafing through a study of early empiricism and came across the case of the so-called 'Bishop' Fortuna. This man, an early example of a scientist, I suppose (never at all a bishop), claimed for some reason, and against all possibility, to be a direct descendent of Irene of Athens, whom conventional history attributes with the honour of gouging out the eyes of her only son. He was still young and childless and soon after died, thus ending his claims to the Byzantine throne and Irene's line. Fortuna poured scientist, theologian and artist into the crucible of himself, for perhaps the last time such a feat was possible – and as indeed had not been possible for many centuries prior – and wrote a series of impenetrable treatises on phenomena whose basis, not being borne out by the developments in science, has been discredited and thereby – like their author – thrown into a barely retrievable darkness. To his contemporaries, so I learned from this study, Fortuna was no such peripheral, being rather a notorious figure of contention in the early academies of England, France and Germany. While Thomas Browne and Roger Bacon were tentatively enumerating common observations – lighting, so to speak, a candle in the great cavern of time and seeing almost nothing but a few motes within a greater darkness, perhaps a little glistening of damp on the wall – Fortuna undertook a series of grand experiments using machines of his own devising, intending to propel himself far into the truth of being, illuminating all. He designed and built a flying machine, not for the purpose of flight in itself but merely as a means best to observe the pattern of waves and tides, believing that they were the 'air' of our island thrown into turbulence by the earth's watery breathing. While his contemporaries salvaged materials from the ocean floor lost to sinking with the aid of diving bells which could only creep down to a maximum depth of one hundred feet before the divers became disorientated by the effects of the pressure, the 'Bishop', by his own account, descended in a contraption resembling a boot to the foot of the Norway Deep, over two thousand feet below the surface, a feat entirely impossible, for by doing so he would have needed to defy the effects of nitrogen narcosis and oxygen toxicity which would not be circumvented by technological developments for over two hundred years after his death. Except, his works contain engravings of species of fish (most prominently, the greater argentine and roundnose grenadier) as well as a number of sea sponges only found at depths greater than one thousand feet. At some time in the early 1660s, in late middle age, Fortuna became convinced that each and every tree around the globe was associated in some serious and necessary way with each and every other, and almost all of his remaining work is devoted exclusively to investigating his conception of the great wooden bole he believed to reside at the centre of the earth, as if a production from God's lathe, and from which the woods of these trees sprouted like whiskers from a face. Throughout the manuscript of his later work one can find scribbled in the margin in repeated instances the phrase, a kind of catechistic pronouncement on his own unsuccess in science: 'The greatest invention in all mankind's history is the horse.' Never does any mention of horses enter the body of his published works, but this pronouncement appears over sixty times as a marginal gloss commenting on his own work in only five works produced between 1632 and 1648. It is as if all the horses were standing outside and looking in, and observing this mad human realm filled with words which seem very often only capable of meaning something by utter chance.

If Bishop Fortuna's work, and by extension his name, is little known, his final work, an ostensible treatise on chess only recently discovered in manuscript in a crooked little attic in Utrecht, is hardly likely to change that. For over nine hundred pages, the reader is taken not through a comprehensive history of the game, nor yet is he or she given an account of the problems, endgames, specific rivalries, nor of the developments of the language of the game as a response to the requirements of its players. Indeed, there is hardly any mention of the specific players of the game, nor to any particular games which, if we turn to other writers on chess, have become part of its mythos. In Bishop Fortuna's study, we are treated to what is essentially a structural analysis, under the forms of chess, of the life he has lived and which he sees stretching out before him, until the toppling of his own personal king at its abrupt end – which, indeed, he accurately foresaw taking place on the Plano del Palazzo Reale in Palermo, a city to which he had never before been and was only compelled to visit by the rising of a storm which chased the ship he was aboard, bound from Tunis to Rome, into the Sicilian port. The marble flagstones of the particular square upon which he died alternate by hue between a pale rose and a deep teal grey. They resemble in their combination a chessboard: though one whose edges are not limited to eight-by-eight columns and rows but seem, by some trick of the architect's design, to extend between, beneath and beyond the buildings which enclose and stand upon the board, and thence across the whole island of Sicily, mapping out in fine detail as they run down to the sea, those lines of longitude and latitude which had first been imagined only a little distance away in Cyrene two millennia earlier.

It is true that, in his study of chess, Bishop Fortuna does refer on occasion to historical sources and precedents, demonstrating a particular liking for abstruse poetic references, for example the *Vetvia*, a thirteenth-century Latin poem, from which he quotes (in his own translation): 'But he defil'd the game who first played at it with dyce, for the chesseman will languish unmoved unlesse the chaunce of the dyce bee to move it: and this has onely been done, because fewe know how to playe slowly, or otherwise for hope of gayne.' In a curious marginal note, Fortuna has asked 'aversion to chaunce godly or ungodly?' Clearly Fortuna saw himself – the very name he chose to adopt declares it – as being subject to chance. Fortuna also quotes from the *De vetula*, 'Of the Old Lady', a long Latin poem from the thirteenth century, in which various games and pastimes are discussed – chess, backgammon, fishing, dice – and their rules, conventions and outcomes likened by analogy to the world around the author. Fortuna showed particular interest in an account of the chess pieces standing for the known cosmos (one which is followed by the same expression of distaste for the dice which we have already noted):

> The King is the Sun, the Pawn Saturn, the Knight Mars, the royal Maid (regia virgo) Venus, the Aufin, himself a Bishop (episcopus), Jupiter; and the wandering Rook the Moon. Mercury is the promoted Pawn. Chess is a noble game so long as it is played in moderation and is not played to amass money. To play with the help of dice is to defile it; the man who first did this either could not appreciate a slow game, or was greedy of gain.

At various moments through the manuscript, invariably when some obtrusion or other rises up in the path of the author, a little engraved icon of the wandering man, though here carrying a chessboard, is set into the text, as if writing was the bedrock from which this prison – life – had been hewn, and a stylised version of the initials 'Zz' is placed above or below, and sometimes within the frame of the engraving itself, like an insect come to annoy him on this unending pilgrimage. 'Zz', as the context shows (or so the author of this study writes), can only stand for *Zugzwang*, and yet the term – literally 'move-compulsion' in English – was not adopted in chess-playing circles until, at the earliest, the beginning of the nineteenth century. Clearly *Zugzwang*, which denotes in chess the necessity under the rules of the game of taking a move, and yet the predicament of any move, no matter how played, being to place the mover in a less fortuitous position, held a great significance for Fortuna. The *Zz* walking man icons are like flags in the text which mark out critical moments in the journey of this person through his life. It is as if Bishop Fortuna were at these instances of his life story picking up a great gavel and pounding the page with frustration at what had been served for him, and what he must now, by the thou-shalt of the hammer blow, by law carry out for and by himself. It is touching to read of how, following the death of his daughter, Fortuna felt, at various points throughout the days and weeks after, a great dragging feeling in his innards which forced him to sit down whenever and wherever it occurred. When he set up his pieces upon the board, he could not shake from his mind the conviction that he was setting up multiple games in multiple places at once, as if in his square he did as he did, and yet this was mirrored in some room of time elsewhere at once, and this doubling itself doubled, and so on until the number became monstrous, each node connected to another throughout all imagined space and time, and to tip one's king was to observe a great and universal loss throughout existence, a stream of falling figures with a clattering of tiny thunder which would tear through the fabric of life.

Most curious of all, in view of the widespread conviction of Fortuna's time that death would come when God willed it, and that the individual, though he or she might regret departing this world before such and such could be achieved, would submit willingly to this will – most curious of all is that the *Zz* icon appears in multitudes at the very end of Fortuna's 'lifebook' in a chequered pattern which spreads across the final page just as did the flagstones of the square in Palermo, implying, as well as many other things (not least that Fortuna foresaw the place of his own death), that at the point between life and death there rises up a choice between one badness and another, and death is only chosen because the continuation of one's living is worse. This is not so unusual. A common feature of the suicide note of highly successful individuals, regardless of culture or era, is a bald and matter-of-fact statement that living is no longer a pleasure, only a burden, and that ending such a life is the only rational thing a person placed in such a predicament would undertake to do. The very reasonableness of death.

Contrary to the impression created by this account of Fortuna's work, he was a vivacious and humorous man, whose writing is peppered with mischievous wit and a love of puns which, though sometimes laboriously manufactured, are generally indicative of a cheerful disposition. Nowhere is this feeling more apparent than in a passage where he describes the game of chess – or perhaps it is something else described under the form of chess – by which he won a no-name gelding whom he subsequently dubbed Mee, and which as we shall see altered the remainder of his life utterly.

'And if you do not know by now,' (so he wrote) 'what it is I hide or don't hide under my wovens, then Chance may prick you. Mee, which is to say us, our friend, will ride shod or not over ye, and whosoever is the steed and whosoever the rider time shall tell, and time shall change as well.'

In Fortuna's history of himself, from this moment he and his horse become confused with each other, perhaps only grammatically at first. Soon, though, it is irrefutable that they really and truly began to combine one with the other until Me and Mee in the text – both common Tudor forms for the first person singular accusative case of the personal pronoun – is interchangeable, apparently both singular and plural, as well as both nominative and accusative. The relationship which Fortuna develops with the horse he won seems to have caused him to go over his old works and make those comments in the margins propounding the importance of the animal.

From this point, Fortuna sees all the world through his twin obsessions of the horse and chess, and any historical material is selected on the basis of its pertinacity as regards equine superiority on the chessboard. So, for example, Fortuna quotes from the twelfth-century Hebrew poem *Shah-mat*, attributed to Abraham ben Meir Ibn Ezra, 'The foot of the Horse (*sūs*) is very light in the battle; / He goes by a crooked path, / His ways are crooked and not straight, / Three houses are his boundaries.' Without any justification, the crookedness of the horse's movement on the board he interprets as a clue or analogy to the fundamental physical and metaphysical function of matter.

He also quotes at length from a chapter of William Caxton's *Game and Playe of the Chesse*, published in 1474, a translation of Cessolis' *Liber de moribus hominum et officiis nobilium*, entitled '*The sixthe chapitre of the thirde book treteth of the sixth pawn, whiche is lykened to taverners hostelers and vitayllers*', and in which a thief is apprehended by a horse. 'Hit happend on a tyme in the parties of lomberdye in the cyte of Iene y't a noble man was logged in an hostelerye wyth moche compaignye. And whan they had gyuen prouendour to their horses In the first oure of the nyght, the seruant of the hous cam secretly to fore y'e horses for to stele away their prouender. And whan he cam to the lordes hors, The hors caught wyth his teth his Arme and helde hit faste that he myght not escape. And whan the theef sawe that he was so strongly holden he began to crye for the grete payne that he suffryd and felte In suche wyse that the noble mannes meyne cam with the hooste. But in no maner ner for ought they coude doo. They coude not take the theef out of the horses mouth vnto the tyme that the neyghbours whiche were noyed wyth the noyse cam and sawe hit. And than the theef was knowen and taken and brought to fore the Iuge And confessid the feet and by sentence diffinytyf was hanged and lost his lyf. And in the same wyse was an other that dyde so. And the hors smote hym in the visage That the prynte of the horse shoo and nayles abode euer in his visage.'

The characteristic medieval ending of a story with another which echoes it presents the interesting case of an animal making a sign out of a human's face, one by which can be read that human's nefarious tendencies. Five hundred years later, animals – and it is no different for humans – are liberated from the allegorical world, and kick for no reason. I noted that Stumpf, in his account of Clever Hans, reported that this incomparably gifted horse had no compunction about kicking his stablehand in the face with a blow that nearly killed him, and all for merely attempting to muck his stable out.

★

When my brother was very young, no more than three years old, a friend of the family paid a visit. She was not used to the company of young children, and remained standing in an attitude of awkwardness as he came into her space and talked the important talk of the three-year-old at her without prelim-inaries. He hugged and touched her; and then, with a change of attitude, a stilling and refocusing of the attention, he put his head up against the lower part of her abdomen in concentrated silence. Having done so, he drew back, looked up, and said, 'You are going to have a baby.' After this, he walked off into the other room, and the dusk of memory descends again. Several weeks later – or so the story goes – the visitor, who had been as puzzled as everyone else by this performance, discovered that she was indeed pregnant.

Alchemist, charlatan, prestidigitator, trickster, illusionist, extra-sensory perceptor, seer, prophet, Puck – or perhaps just a human. What might you be and have been?

He, my brother, claimed to be able to remember far back into his infancy. He could describe into adulthood the yarn colours and tricot stitch of the blanket which covered him in his push-chair. It was not unusual for him to see or smell something and be reunited, as he would then describe it, with an earlier form of himself, one even before language. For a long time he was obsessed with reincarnation; latterly, with the design of a working time machine.

At times he went too far. I can distinctly remember my brother describing the experience of being born. We were sat in a run-down Victorian pub, about a little scar-topped table, smoking, and he described how it felt to come out into the world in naked bodily littleness. But, like the canniest tricksters – though also it must be admitted like those liars whose imagination fails them under demand of detail – he did not offer specifics. This memory, of the discussion of his remembered birth, unlike most does not fade out because this little performance of his – of ours, per-haps – was interrupted by my noticing across the room, though only two or three tables distant, not far enough for comfort, one man give to another a roll of notes, and that other pass to him, without precaution of concealment in a bag or beneath a hat, the shocking form of a true and real gun.

*

Up at the top of Pilot Hill it felt like I could see over Winchester, Southampton and Portsmouth all the way down to the sea, but of course that was impossible. Looking over the fields and the hedges which divide them, far across the undulating land, all I could imagine was war. Earlier, I had been reading about horses and about Agincourt, which probably presents a similar view to the one before me. A summary account of the battle is enough to reveal the proportion and shape of the glory of war.

The battle took place on a freshly ploughed field following heavy rain, so that the charging French infantry, wearing full heavy steel armour, were exhausted wading through knee-deep mud before they even reached the English line. At the time the charge was commanded and begun, large numbers had left their ranks to get warm or feed their horses. The cavalry came first, but the English arrow wounds to French horses sent them into a frenzied panic, whereby they stampeded their own troops to death. The advancing French forces were so tightly packed by the slowness of the first line's advance, and hemmed in by woods on either side, that the rows of men were crushed up against one another, tripping over the dead in front, and landed on by those behind, until all were a sitting target. Those still standing could not use their swords because of the crush. There is evidence that infantrymen who fell or were knocked over drowned or suffocated in their helmets. Those who fell and did not drown could not get back up and were slaughtered as they writhed around in the mud. Two-thirds of the French army and one sixth of the English were killed in three hours. The battle is notable, apart from for its pivotal role in the unfolding of the Hundred Years' War, for being that in which range weaponry, particularly in the form of the English longbows, first showed its efficacy.

Fifty miles south-east from Agincourt, five hundred and one years later, Allied armies spent four and a half months moving the Western Front five miles east. The number of dead from both sides produced by this fighting – approximately one million men – is consistent, proportionally, with the figures at Agincourt, if Agincourt's approximately 8-10,000 dead in one day is multiplied by the number of days of the Somme offensive. Thus, or so it struck me as I looked out over the fields of the Downs, perhaps war is a machine which works always at the same tempo, indifferent to man's degree of technological development, one which is, as it were, a manner of time itself. It is as if war, by grinding bodies into meat, keeps the days turning over, maintains the production of history, draws the best out of nations, which must produce and produce people and more sophisticated machines and counter-machines without cessation, so that we at home can carry on living.

The horse, as 'Bishop' Fortuna said, is humanity's greatest invention. It is indeed a delightful machine. The War Horse Memorial in Ascot, unveiled on 8 June 2018, commemorates, to quote the information on their website, 'the millions of UK, Allied and Commonwealth horses, mules and donkeys lost during The Great War. It pays tribute to the nobility, courage, unyielding loyalty and immeasurable contribution these animals played in giving us the freedom of democracy we all enjoy today, and signifies the last time the horse would be used on a mass scale in modern warfare.' It is estimated that eight million horses died in the conflict from machine-gun fire and shelling, but also from disease, starvation and exhaustion. To take one language from each major family of the Indo-European dynasty, to experience the similarities in form across them, faint echoes across time, between Greek, Dutch, Gaelic, French and Polish – this is to bear witness to horses. It was the domestication of horses which allowed the spread of our protolanguage, a language for which we can supply no name except in relation to our own, from the people of the Pontic–Caspian Steppe as they swept across Europe. It was the horse that allowed just five hundred Spaniards, led by Hernando Pizarro, to ride out of hiding in the buildings around the enormous square of Cajamarca, kill seven thousand unarmed Inca in the course of only two hours, pull Atahualpa from his parrot-feathered litter and imprison him – Atahualpa, who was a deity born of the sun, so revered that he spat unwanted food into the hands of his wives and compelled them to eat any hairs which fell on his clothing in the avoidance of sorcery.

The horse has now been replaced by the tank, train, car and lorry, but like those others it remains a delightful machine.

★

One day in the latter part of my stay at the cottage in the South Downs a pipe burst under the kitchen units, and, not knowing where the mains tap was, I lay on the floor being sprayed with water, and thought to myself, there can be no end to this. Fortunately it occurred to me that I could turn the tap on above me, relieve the pressure down here a little, and buy some time to find the stopcock – which in actual fact was in the cupboard directly next to where I had lain on the dirty wet tiles. Between calls to plumbers – none would answer the phone – I undertook some first researches, idly and with little conviction, into the history of cremation. I noted that Professor Gorini of Lodi, Italy, was invited to visit this country and supervise the erection of an apparatus, assisted by Mr William Eassie, the Cremation Society's Honorary Secretary. On 17 March 1879, the body of a horse was cremated and, on seeing how completely and rapidly it was reduced to ashes, Sir Henry Thompson later observed that it foreshadowed the result which numerous actual cremations have since realised, namely, that by this process complete combustion of an adult human body is effected in from one to two hours and is so perfectly accomplished that no smoke or effluvia escapes from the chimney.

Just as the landline began to peal with a returned phone call, I recalled that time, so the physicists say, only occurs because of heat.

★

—How do you feel for me?

I approach you through the fields, where the river flows, into the wood, through all the tangled thickets, the grey fibrous stems of the brambles knotted up, a clue at the world's unsweptness if it were not for people. I pass through all this – or I have already passed through it – and now I find myself there on the fringe of a clearing with trees, in a little hollow, and I am looking up, and you are not there, but your tree is there, I can sense the tremor of it, as if it were a soundless sound, and there is a scattering of light, there is a goodness.

—I was a good child. I do not mean in behaviour. I was a good and happy child.

Yes.

—I was good like a chestnut is good. When I was a child I was almost perfect like each chestnut is different and yet perfect. I was so happy. We ran over the great bowed fields, scattered the livestock, lived in the outdoors; always at and over the frontiers. Did you know that I never feared a thing in my life?

Yes.

—My mum—

(Why is it that we use words like this, 'my', not 'our' or even just 'mum'? The words are so small and well worn, they are so null. How to fit everything that she is, and me, and you, and the network of nerves between, and not have only a nullity, a nothing?)

This is how the words turned from you, like a turning of birds, and the bellies of meaning hidden and shearing off. Tell me, how was it, when the significations first began to slide off of the signs?

—My mum said that it was Joe killing himself that did it, that made me fear death. He killed himself, and she came to me and said, 'Uncle Joe is dead,' and all my hair fell out, but never did I fear death. I cannot say better, but it cannot be, because never did I fear death. How can a child say what it is that makes all his hair fall out overnight. How can a child say anything. My hair fell out in a circle at the crown of my head. I looked like I was to enter the Order with a perfect circle tonsure, for how should I live were Euclid ashamed of me.

Here, I am caused to speak, though who can know if any sound I make:

—Circles are older than Euclid, don't you know. Didn't we ride eight thousand years ago out of the steppe on wagons with wheels and conquer ourselves?

—You don't understand mathematics, a wheel is not a circle, so you should try not to speak when mathematics is the subject. Have you ever read Euclid?

—No.

—Well, you should. Euclid's definition of a circle was this: 'A circle is a plane figure bounded by one line, and such that all right lines drawn from a certain point within it to the bounding line are equal. The bounding line is called its circumference and the point its centre.'

Sometimes it is true that I enter into the talk, but generally I sit and I hear his voice in my voice telling me things I never knew.

—I prefer his definition of a point. It is the first figure of the Elements which he defines, because without a point, there is no starting or finishing, and yet any given point has no existence. It is a most beautiful conception.

I listen as I sit, I listen as I ride. I listen through the days, and into the dark.

—1. A point is that of which there is no part.

It makes no sense, but I understand it, and I'm not sure how I know to tell it myself.

★

Before I came to this little house which I did not know I needed, I often did not make it to bed at all but would jerk awake still sitting in my chair in the utter dark. Then, in the deep of the night, I would be forced by the cold and a distended bladder to rise and walk past the kitchen window and as I did so I must force myself to look only forwards, like an army under command of no one but itself and fearful as a consequence, because I might see you outside, on the other side of the window, pacing, smoking, with that look on your face, perturbed by the bad behaviour of the primes or some such, impatient with the conventions of all humanity, especially the use of night for sleeping. I wonder if you and the great Kurt Gödel, master mathematician who starved himself to death out of fear of poisoning, discuss the matter of logic. Is suicide in some way that proof of the incompleteness theorem? The stitch that leads from the known to what lies beyond it? Is killing yourself the way to prove that life is only an enclosed system, that it is a construction of itself? But what does the act discover beyond? What is that moment of death? What was that moment at which the signs turned – were turned – like the tips to the butcher's hooks, and there was no way back?

Now that I am here, in somebody else's house, and though doing little different than I would be if I were home, the proportion of things seems to be coming back, time laying itself out in such a way as it can be understood, even if this is not the way it actually is, and sleep coming gently for me at night, and waking as gently at the beginning of the day. The brutality which ran as a rich seam at the borderline between mind and body – the market for it has vanished, the quarrying has stopped. One day, I understand, I will forget to think of you, through one whole day, but not yet.

*

I rode through the undulating lanes of the Downs and sometimes he was with me and sometimes he was not. His life became a story I told myself inwardly, in order to what? I do not want to forget, but I want to forget.

He removed himself from conventional education, simply ceasing to attend – this, not any behavioural issue, was the cause of the expulsions – and immersed himself at the town library in the study of peoples exhibiting forms of cultural existence which he found more conducive to his nature and needs, Amazonian tribes who had never seen a white man or cotton clothes. Couldn't he have been another Rousseau? Might we all? One night, between the end of my final exams and graduation, my girlfriend at the time and I returned from town – I was then living in Reading – at about one in the morning and discovered, in my bed, my brother. I knew by the smell before I even turned on the light that he was there. He had cycled from Colchester with no shoes on. That was in 1998. In the ten days before he died – in Spring 2015 – he ran into the woods which fringe the river Stour at the border of Essex and Suffolk, coming out as far as I know only once to beg food and water from a pub, from which he fled as soon as the police arrived – they were called because here, manifestly, was a lunatic or someone in need: someone beyond what is human. He had no bedding, no spare clothes. It is hard to imagine how unpleasant it must be to live in the woods in late April without shelter, food or water for ten days, when what one's imagination wants to do is tell us it was an Arcadia, which evidently it was not. But he had taken a three-inch knife from the knife block – this would be his shelter.

*

If I come down the path from our old childhood front door, through the white picket fence and head up the lane over the fragrant fallen pine needles, a sheet of silken slipperiness beneath my feet, which slide them down with the camber of the little twisted road, soon there is the church at the top of the road, thrusting up in vertical resistance against the slant of the land down to the left, a resistance appearing to have real and true will to it – and who can speak of norths and souths and easts and wests in that land of childhood where the myths live on. If, now, I take a map before me of a place lived in and loved, the irresemblance it bears to reality is appalling. There is a taste of insanity in looking at that map, reading the familiar names but sensing that this true relationship between them has been hidden from everyone living there. Sensing that the map lacks a fundamental grasp on reality like a dictionary does, because it fails to account for feeling, because it is only as it were gossiping among itself and retelling in-jokes about space.

If I reach the junction at the foot of the flintstone wall, above which the church hulks, and turn left down the hill, soon the incline levels off at the little stream which runs beneath the road, and the bridge, a bridge which is barely a bridge at all, still houses beneath its low arch the creatures which it did when we were young, fol-dee-roll. And if I continue walking, past the pub, the places beyond become less loved and known, and the strength of that familiarity wanes like the heat from a fire with distance, until the road winds off into obscurity, where there is only darkness and cold. But now, if I walk, and continue walking, beyond what is known and loved, the road disappears, or winds down without me much noticing to become a track, a path, trodden grass, nothing, and then I find myself standing before your tree again, and it seems every little winding road in the nation leads there, inescapable you.

There are so many nows that the tenses fail us. There would need to be a greater delicacy to words to frame the way time has with you and with me, and the fine silk threads and seeds, pollen grains and motes, which brush past us through the pulses of now between.

★

It was at that little bridge, hardly a bridge at all, perceptible for the motorists coming through the village only as the lowest point of a shallow valley, and in the narrowing of the road – yes, it was at the little bridge where the road narrowed that you instigated that grand illusion at dusk which caused drivers to panic, brake as hard as they ever had, fill the air with a howl and the quick tang of scorched rubber (the whole world turns only because of a burning) and shout out wordless complaint, wordless because an adult should never be humiliated by a child, it is meant to be the other way round. He – you – required nothing but a partner, and where he cooked up this scheme I cannot say, but it worked every time. He took whoever it was down to the little bridge which was hardly a bridge at all, and they stood on opposite sides of the road under the dusklight which every child yearns to hold onto, which we chase out into the air through doorways and up all the little lanes of the country for just another minute of play, pleading by play with the day to hold out a little longer. He and his partner – sometimes it was me, sometimes someone else – stood one on each side of the little road where it narrows and as the chosen car drew down the hill we stood in readiness. And when, like a thrown ball in the air about to turn and drop, the moment was quite right, he gave the sign and we crouched down and took hold of two ends of an imaginary rope, lifted, and leaned back into the weight of each other, stretching nothing-at-all taut over the road in an illusion there at the little bridge which was hardly a bridge at all. How else is a child to have power in this world than in pranks like these?

166

★

In a marvellous portent of the inevitable end of culture there can be found a Wikipedia page dedicated to all known hoax Wikipedia articles. (It is incredibly hot, far too hot for cycling, or gardening, or even sitting, and so it is that I am lying in my pants on the floor aimlessly wandering through the labyrinth of the internet.) This page, though incomplete ('many hoaxes remain undiscovered'), includes links to articles – now stamped with a hoax warning – about fictional people (a Chinese Bishop; a brevet American Civil War General, and claimed inventor of cream soda; a rapist from nineteenth-century New Orleans; an eighteenth-century oil and forestry magnate working in South America; a New Mexico Lobos American football team member; a murder victim from Bridgeport, Connecticut; a British naval commander who fought – or did not fight – Emperor Napoleon Bonaparte; a TV actress; a Scottish minister; numerous gurus and mystics; a dandy called Guy de la Bretaigne; the inventor of a new form of popcorn; and many others). Many other links lead to articles concerning imaginary attributes or facts about real people (that Lord Byron kept a crocodile and a honey badger for pets; that Hans Geiger's nickname was Gengar; that Henry II of France had an illegitimate daughter called Elaine de Francias; and, again, many more). There are numerous links to fake businesses or organisations (Mendaxi, a fake Greek cosmetics firm; Milk Studios from Sweden; and so on). Articles about numerous bands (Blood Eagle, a UK thrash metal band named after a probably fictitious method of medieval torture in which the ribs are separated from the spine and the lungs are drawn through the incision made there in imitation of wings); Napalm Brain from an unspecified place in Britain; Ted and the Treble Tones from Fresno; The Falsetto Basses from North Carolina; The Brothers Wing from Florida; The Vans Brothers from New Zealand; etc.).

Articles concerning several torture devices, usually medieval (Crocodile Shears; Spanish Tickler; Peace Breaker's Muzzle); regarding a fictional public institution, namely the Library of Amartya in (or not in) South Delhi (nor, indeed, anywhere). Finally, in an account given of a prize, purportedly established by the Japan Academy (which, having been founded in 1879, continues to really and truly exist), in recognition of Outstanding Achievement in Winning an Outstanding Achievement Award.

Sometimes, when I consider the unreality of everything around me, I wonder if in fact you performed at that tree the final act of Puckishness, faked a death, and are out there still, wandering the fields, laughing at the sun and the buzzing of the flies within its light, the rope of your trickery still thrumming to the tune of it, and Death stepping out of his car door and shaking a fist that he was duped like any ordinary driver by your trick with the rope.

*

Only a few days of my stay at the old house in Woodhay remained when my reading brought me to a book written by William Charles Plenderleath called *The White Horses of the West of England*, first published in 1885. The author's name sounded familiar, and, glancing down the columns of books piled beside my bed, I discovered that I had already read the same author's earlier work, *The Parish Priest's Visiting List, with a Few Remarks on Parochial Visitation*, from 1858. I say that I read it; most of the little book, no bigger than a pocket notebook – for that was where it was intended to be carried – was taken up with tickets for the parish poor. These were printed as little templates which the coal merchant, grocer, fishmonger, butcher, and so on and so forth, took as payment for their goods, later to be reimbursed by the Church. Plenderleath, still a young man, shortly before his move to Cherhill, where he eventually worked as parish priest for over thirty years, came up with this idea as a system of exchange. Although no mention is made of it in his *Memoranda* (another in the pile which I had consumed) the initial scheme must have been deemed a success, because Plenderleath was asked to produce a book of such tickets, with a brief introduction giving an account of their uses – and it was this introduction that I had read and remembered. The Reverend found himself writing the introduction to a book which he knew would be produced in great quantity, which would travel out across the nation to the farthest-flung parishes, across the sea even, and up the mysterious rivers to the far reaches of the Empire – throughout, in brief, a world which he describes in his introduction, quoting the Ordination charge of the clergy, as 'naughty'. Barely out of the seminary, he felt the urge to dispense, in addition to his instructions on the uses of his tickets, also some choice pieces of advice in regard to the function of the parochial priest in general. Such a one is never off duty; he should wear clothing appropriate to his position at all times; he must never forget his prayer book and visitation list; if he is commencing work in a new parish, he should take care not to be 'too *professional*' at first in order to build a personal relationship before starting the serious work of preaching. 'I remember once going into a cottage in my first parish,' he writes by way of example, 'and finding an ill looking fellow sitting smoking by the fire, playing with a large mastiff, and abusing his wife. The moment I appeared he seized his cap which was lying upon the table, and dashed it on with an evident intention of evincing how little he desired my presence. Without however appearing to notice this, I exclaimed, "What a fine dog you have there," and upon his somewhat sulky reply, pushed on a conversation upon dogs and suchlike subjects, until in his satisfaction at finding a parson who knew something else besides his Bible, he took off his cap, and offered me a seat, and submitted before I left the house, to a carefully worded lecture, as from one man and husband to another, upon the duty of treating his wife kindly.'

As I moved on to his later book, one written this time not in the service of his work for the Church but purely as an expression of his interest in hillside horse monuments, I learned that except for a single one in Aberdeenshire these figures are peculiar to England – though, it is true, imitations have sprung up in Australia and South Africa more recently – and that they were all around me. Plenderleath opens his study with the following words: 'There are few travellers by any of the Western high roads who would not have seen and noticed one or other of those great figures of horses cut out in the chalky hills which form such conspicuous landmarks for a distance of ten miles or more.' Reading on, I discovered that I had cycled through the villages associated with three of these monuments in my rides through the Downs, and yet, contrary to Plenderleath's assessment of the probability, I had never noticed any of these figures, all three of which are at least one hundred and fifty feet long – the Uffington over double this – and placed as the author of this book says on their respective hillsides in prominent view, visible for many miles around. Believing myself to be an observant person, I cannot say that I wasn't surprised, even a little annoyed. The weather having cooled in the preceding days, I resolved that I would cycle to the Uffington White Horse, the closest of the three and the largest and oldest in the country, the following day – a ride of no more than twenty-five miles each way.

★

The following morning I was woken by an alarm at six o'clock; and by seven I was backing the bike I had borrowed for the preceding six weeks out of the outhouse one last time into an already hot day with two rounds of sandwiches, three litres of water and Plenderleath's book strapped to the frame. This bike, although only an old BSA with little to recommend it – the rubber of its tyres was almost completely perished with age, the cheaply chromed handlebars were pocked with rust, and it squeaked and grinded interminably – had to my mind taken on a part of the character of some of the rides we had taken together. With an odd sensation close to embarrassment I noted that I had spent more time with this old machine than with any human being over the preceding year and a half. A hundred and fifty years ago, if not everybody owned a horse, then at least almost everybody knew how to ride one. And those who did own one developed deep feelings for it, stroked and petted it, talked to and soothed it with sounds of the mouth. As I swung down Pebble Hill towards the river once again, this time my last, I felt gravity pull at me, down to the organs inside; and there came the exhilaration of moving quickly and of my own volition in and out from under the canopy of trees; and if there had been a rambler on the verge who could have sworn they heard a cyclist making affectionate words to the machine he rode on, then I wouldn't dispute it.

It was not long before the revolutions of my feet, rocking of my hips, snaking of my back and bobbing of my head all fell into a rhythm with my breathing, and it is in this state that my mind is most liable to discover and pick at those infinities which are hid, to return to Blake's phrase, if only within myself.

*

If you watch a lone child play you'll see him or her as it were fold down into itself like a piece of paper, smalling and smalling, turning in, down to the tiny things, because it's here that the greatest value can be found, though who can know why. There was the time you were lost at the beach and Mum and Dad looked for you for three hours, and I must have been looking too, beneath a hand being held and tugged in antagonised distress over the undulating sand littered with broken shells and gritty shale, but I can't remember. In the end you were not drowned, dead or taken but several miles away with an excellent collection of little feathers and tiny shells and no knowledge of being missing. If it was that I could hear your voice, if it was that you could speak: I was and am and never will be missing, your voice will say to me somehow.

That memory is not even a memory at all. It's something I know happened, and there are a few scatterings of beachiness in the high wind of my brain, but I don't believe any of it. How can we know.

*

I rode on and on, deep in that rhythm of progression, myself and this machine working together in a way that felt miraculous, on my way to visit this giant horse, and all I could think of was what is small, recalled in voices that flowed through me effortlessly. Maybe I am as contrary as you were.

'I do not recall when first I developed this intense interest in miniaturism,' wrote S. B. J. Skertchly in a letter of 1881 to a young student. 'In a sense I suppose it is a retreat from what preoccupies me in my daily work. I do remember very clearly when young begging to be allowed to take my father's saddle in because I was so deeply affected by the smallness and perfection of a design depicting a standing horse embossed upon its horn, although of course I did not begin the collection of miniatures until adulthood.'

This was only three years after Skertchly's discovery of the prehistoric use of fire at Beeches Pit, and of the publication of his second book, *The Physical System of the Universe: An Outline of Physiography.*

'After the accident,' he continues (here he refers to a shard of chert which penetrated the cornea of his right eye during a geological survey), 'when I was forbidden to read and warned of the dangers to my sight, I put my books away in fright and spent whole afternoons in the easy chair with my eyes closed against the light, and it was not the objects and people most familiar to me which came into my sightless vision (irrespective of any degree of effort expended, I have always found it impossible to picture the faces of the people most close to me, which perhaps accounts for the extent of my fearfulness at that time, for I was very close to losing my sight) but rather the little standing horse on my father's saddle which I had neither seen nor thought of for over twenty years.'

Repeated and ongoing excavations of Beeches Pit since Skertchly's discovery of it have revealed a number of hearths from various times, one of these carbon-dated to 400,000 years ago, the earliest evidence of the use of fire by humans in Britain. The distribution of fragments of flint about the hearth suggests knapping took place gathered about this fire, down at the hearth hollow in the soil. Skertchly could have had no idea of the extension of time which separated himself from these crouching flint knappers in the woods, knocking off flakes so thin as to be translucent, as light and diaphanous as the wings of flies, little filaments of flesh, but it was large enough in his mind to be as indistinct as the face of his wife to the imagination as he sat there in convalescence with the patch pulled down over his eye, dreaming of the structurations which might or might not be discovered to connect the stars, seeing the little horse and waiting to be better enough to begin working again. Skertchly, drawing to a conclusion in his letter, advises the student to concentrate on littlenesses, because what is little is meant to be played with, but what is big forbids us, and it is by play that we discover the things that matter to us.

I recalled how Skertchly had begun collecting miniature animal sculptures after being given a gift by a colleague, a quartz elephant which this colleague had been told was ancient but which actually was one of thousands which were then being made by small children and sold in the bazaars of Lahore to credulous tourists. I remembered your feathers, and the tiny conch shells you had gathered, so small and beautifully crafted that we turned them on our childhood palms for hours on end, imagining what worlds were held within the dark interior even as adults brushed them aside by the dozen as grit which imperilled the picnic. This remembrance brought to mind the discovery, long after Skertchly's death, of a sculpture at Kostenki XI, an archaeological site a hundred miles from the Ukrainian border in south-western Russia, depicting a mammoth at a scale of 1:400. This object, depicting the largest land mammal then living, is formed from a piece of marl the size of a single baked bean. What pressure of desire was it that drove the sculptor to depict the terrestrial giant which roamed about in the Siberian wilderness beyond the walls of the hut, itself made from mammoth bone, to bring that enormous living thing out of – or was it into? – such a small space of stone?

As I rode under the trees and felt the alternating heat and cold which their shade created, I thought about the smallness of that mammoth sculpture, of Skertchly's collection, of the mysterious effect of the very small on the human mind. There is something about these tiny made objects which seems to drop a keyhole down into the everyday world through which we cannot stop ourselves from bending down to, and seeing what we can see. And here I was, halfway to a three-thousand-year-old geoglyph over four times longer than the blue whale skeleton which as a child I distinctly remember standing beneath at the Natural History Museum and looking up at in no more or less wonder than I had when peering into the tiny curved aperture of those shells which my brother had brought home from the beach.

*

It was not much further on that I saw the first sign for Uffington. From that point I could count down from the old painted cast iron waymarkers how many miles distant I was from the village in whole miles, then halves, then quarters. I scanned the fields to left and right of me – I had failed either to bring a map or to look for the exact location of the horse, north, south, east or west, about the town in advance of setting out – and it was only when I very nearly went into a ditch filled with a tangle of brambles while looking for the horse that I decided to slow down and take the opportunity to look around properly. In front of me lay the village; to my right the crooked lanes wriggled along the field boundaries down to the river; to my left the fields swelled up into grazing pasture and arced over some hills beyond my sight. This last direction seemed to present the most probable location of the horse, and so I continued, looking now only left as I went, but still I could see nothing, nor a route to get up on to that higher ground. The road brought me into the village, where I thought it best to follow signs to the horse. However, in efforts not to collide with parked cars or holidaying pedestrians, the latter of whom seemed also to be taking a break from the customary uses of a pavement, I did not see a single sign for the horse. As the main road took me in a loop round the village several times, and as the degree of my distraction increased, so it was that when I stopped I couldn't work out which road I had come in on, nor where those hills I had seen lay, the trees and buildings of the village obscuring my view of the countryside which surrounded it. It was probably close to an hour later that I stood either side of the frame of that old grey-blue BSA up in the hills above the village, the salt of my sweat stinging into the tips of my eyes, filled with a sense of defeat. During the Second World War, the Uffington horse was covered over with turf and branches of brush so that the pilots of the Luftwaffe, who had flown hundreds of miles from the airfields of Belgium and the Netherlands, could not navigate by its unmissable shape, which could be seen from many thousands of feet above sea level and from a dozen miles distant – and yet I, down on the ground where it had been dug, exploring through all the lanes around the village for an hour, could find no trace. I wondered if the horse, which I knew from Plenderleath's study required regular cleaning in order to remain visible – for first the chalk turned green with algae, moss and mould, and then the grass and soil crept over its edges seeking to cover it up – yes, I wondered in that way I find I have with fate whether it was only when I discovered the existence of the horse and attempted to visit it that the three-thousand-year-old monument had fallen into decline and been allowed to disappear into the earth in hiding from me.

Eventually, I discovered that the horse was still of course extant, and that I was merely too close to it to see it for what it was – its anatomy was lost in the closeness, and the chalk lines resembled nothing more than slippages of earth on the hillside which had opened up the whiteness of its underneath to view. After eating a sandwich close by one of the animal's hind hooves, I cycled out west from the village and its horse, turning regularly to watch it recede and thereby assume a shape which I could appreciate. The sun was now right above me, and in places the road had melted and the bitumen seams begun to run. In the worst cases large rectangles of shingled tarmac had slid and sheared over the solid strata beneath, like floes of half crusted lava. The further I rode on, and the further the horse receded behind me, the more it struck me from its appearance as I turned back to look at it – I even thought to take a photograph – that this was not a horse in the slightest, but rather some unknown animal that either the ancient inhabitants of this part of the world had invented, or that they had hunted to extinction, or perhaps that had begun as one animal but by long process of mutation during the seven yearly cleanings by which its continuation was ensured had become quite another, one with no existence.

*

That night, my last at the house on the Downs, I messaged the picture I had taken of the Uffington White Horse to a friend who I knew used to keep horses – *doesn't look much like a horse to me*, I said. To which her immediate reply was: *yea, it's the wrong way round*. This was not at all the reply I was expecting. I puzzled at the effect this statement had made on me, and at the manner in which it had been meant – was she in earnest or joking? I realised that it would not have been out of character for her to be both. In the end, just when I had decided not to pay any more attention to the matter, I remembered several occasions walking with this friend and her finding it impossible to walk with me at her left side. In a sudden burst she would say 'No, I can't do it!' and trot round to the other side of me, or pull me across to her right – there – and all was right with the world again. This she had done from the habit of walking horses the customary way, always with one's right shoulder to their left; and when a horse is mounted, it is always mounted from the left; and when a horse is dressed and groomed, it is always from the left. And so, horses, like the moon, are only seen from one side: from the left, facing left. Thus it was that the Uffington White Horse was pointing the wrong way; and thus it was that my suspicions that the horse had never been a horse at all had reason to grow.

I had planned to have an early night so I could get up and clean the house before leaving for my mid-morning train, but the shape my thought had taken, a knot of perplexity that grew more and more tangled as I pulled at it, wouldn't allow me to leave it alone. I sat up in my chair one last time and pursued these horses, or whatever they were, across the hills and into the night.

Of all the many dozens of horse figures found or recorded across England, only four are known to face right: the earlier one at Westbury, now lost, and those at Uffington, Folkestone and Osmington. The hill horses of England, whose almost invariable orientation to the left has perplexed archaeologists specialising in geoglyphs for several hundred years, must by the nature of the horse's relationship with the humans who have used them for so long be oriented upon that left – clearly the archaeologists, like myself, were no equestrians. I concluded that my investigation had to begin by examining the four horses which faced to the right.

Fig. 6.

Fig. 7

Two of these right-facing horses may be discredited immediately. The first of these, the old horse at Westbury, was destroyed over two hundred years ago (the current Westbury horse, which certainly faces to the left, was cut in 1778), but we are fortunate enough, as Plenderleath points out, to have an engraving of it, made in 1772. No documentary evidence for an existence prior to this date can be found for this earlier horse, and yet it seems by its appearance to have been ancient. Unlike any of the other hill horses, this old horse at Westbury, one hundred feet long and nearly as tall, had a crescent on its tail – indicating an association with the divine.

Although the horse is a strange shape, it is certainly a horse – it has a saddle, after all – and it certainly looks to be facing to the right. However, in a map of the area produced in 1773 – five years before the old horse was destroyed and its newer one cut – the horse clearly faces left. This may appear to leave us caught in an insoluble puzzle – the horse can't have faced both left *and* right – until we recollect that in the process of engraving every image is flipped, as if passed before a mirror. Such a process is ordinarily compensated for by engravers, who mirror their source material before engraving it on copper plate, an absolute necessity in the case of printing the written word, for example. Presumably this engraver, the one copying the earlier Westbury Horse, thought a horse, being a natural object, could face any which way. Maps, by contrast, are more sensitive to such reversals; and an engraver who flipped east for west and vice versa would not last long in the profession. So it is that the map presents Bratton Down to the east of Westbury Down, as it is in the world; and so, by virtue of this, we can be assured that the first Westbury white horse faced left, and that the engraver who allowed the horse to face right did not understand that, while a horse might be a natural phenomenon, the way we look at it is not.

Of the three remaining right-facing horses, the one at Folkestone, cut in 2004, can not really be judged to be properly a horse, because this date places its making long after the horse has ceased in general culture to be known intimately by humans, to which that horse's orientation right attests. The argument is manifestly circular, but that makes its conclusion no less true.

Of the last two right-facing horses, the one at Osmington, cut in 1808, presents a unique case, because it is also the only horse, whether facing right or left, which carries a rider. If this secures its identity as 'horse', it places it too in a category separate from those other horse figures: here is a representation entirely of domestication; it is a representation of a human as much as of a horse. Either way, I did not think it disingenuous to declare it beyond my consideration.

Having thrown out all the other right-facing horses from the scope of my researches, I could come, finally to assess the Uffington Horse, the oldest of them all, and also, as we have concluded, the only horse facing right – if of course this singularity we have deduced for it does not negate such a classification as 'horse', as was my suspicion. Certainly many questions arise. Might the Uffington Horse face right because it predates the domestication of horses in these lands and thus was then still free to be seen from either side? (The horses of Lascaux, for example, are depicted running right and running left, and are most certainly horses.) Or, if not preceding this domestication – for the proto-Indo-Europeans rode here from the steppe some six thousand years before its making – perhaps during an interregnum, so to speak, in which the horse liberated itself for a period from human rule and, like the wild horses on Dartmoor, could be seen free, from both sides? Is perhaps the very seeing of horses from their right side that which makes them wild, the dark side of the moon? Did this figure, which had been called 'horse' since the twelfth century at the very latest, have something more subtle to tell?

Browsing late into the night I came across a Fellow of the Royal College of Surgeons and resident of Fontwell, the late Olaf Swarbrick (although his name might seem to indicate a hoax – that he is a troll – it appears that he was a bona fide vet who specialised in game poultry in the south of England; moreover, the identity and reality of the man is immaterial: the thoughts were thought, whether as a hoax or not). Yes, I discovered that, in a letter of October 2010 to the *Veterinary Record* journal written only two months before his death, Swarbrick, who roamed these and other hills across the West Country with his collie, suggested that the horse is in fact a greyhound or wolfhound. This view is by no means one unique to our own time. Already, by 1740, there was doubt being cast as to the identity of the figure, as the Reverend William Asplin wrote (pseudonymously) in 'The Impertinence and Imposture of Modern Antiquaries Displayed, by Philalethes Rusticus': 'Though he has Resemblance enough to be called a Horse as properly as any other quadruped, yet I cannot say He is a Perfect Picture of a Horse. As to his Head, it wants a little repairing. The Rest of His forehead is not so much amiss, especially not at all too short, being from his ears to his withers about fifty of my paces, *i.e.* 150 feet. But then he is quite a *light-bodied* one: I may say for a Horse that has lain so long at grass, carries *no body at all*; insomuch that should he take up hill, were I upon the Back of him, I should be under terrible apprehensions he would slip through his Girth.' Continuing, Asplin (as Rusticus) likens the figure's tail more to a fox's than a horse; and he goes on to make satirical reply to a letter by a Dr Wise, published in a pamphlet of 1738, in which the doctor asserts, with reference to the words of Kranzius (though without indicating how we are to take them), that 'Witichind, upon his conversion from the darkness of Paganism, was the first who took the white colt for his device, in allusion to the brightness of Christianity, having till that time used a black one.' Asplin's reply makes simple use of geology in its rebuttal: 'In a word, whoever will have such sort of Horse must be content with such sort of *Colour* as the country affords, however he may blazon his own arms... I may venture to hold him [i.e. Dr. Wise] a small Wager, that should the Horse scape a scouring but two seven years more his *Dapple* would become a *Green one*, which would be a still greater *Rarity* for all true lovers of Antiquity.' Seeking the truth of the matter, we may make our own judgements based on aerial photographs; a view of the Uffington geoglyph which was of course inaccessible to Dr Wise and William Asplin, even in his guise as Philalethes Rusticus; and even, again, William Plenderleath. However, the evidence supplied in Plenderleath's book implies that the shape of the 'horse' has always been unstable. I once again went back through *The White Horses of the West of England*, seeking the loophole or dropped stitch of the argument, a little assumption or knot of data which would allow me to interpret the material and prove my theory.

Although Plenderleath, in a comparison of his own survey illustration of 1892 to one made in 1735, finds that there is only a very small alteration, we may find, if we compare these two to others made in 1813 and 1835, that the horse in fact appeared to change shape sufficient in the space of a century to allow the doubt to enter our minds (if the copy artists were good and true, of course) that the horse as originally cut in metre-deep pits into the hillside by the original Bronze Age engineers three thousand years ago, may have been any animal at all.

Uffington Horse, 1813   *Uffington Horse, 1835*

Uffington Horse, 1982

Plenderleath does not reproduce the illustration of 1735 in his book, and his assertion from this evidence that the figure exhibits an unchanging shape is contradicted by the later illustration of 1813, in which the horse resembles not a dog this time but rather a cat. While there is an uncertainty as to the provenance and dating of these illustrations, and to the quality of the artistry involved in their production, certain differences of detail, ones which would surely not be misrepresented by the artist, signify that the shape of this animal is and always has been in flux: the detached leg and lack of an eye in the 1813 engraving; the extended right rear heel of the 1892 depiction; the changeable length of the beak or snout – and these are just those examples gleaned from visual reproductions. Further evidence for this instability of appearance comes to us through written evidence, in which the animal has been changing in equipage and company: Lysons' 'Britannia' states that the horse once wore a saddle, while Ralf de Deceto, writing in the 1180s, described the White Horse of Uffington as having a foal at its side.

If we pass through Plenderleath's analysis and then throw it off, if we look simply at the fragments of information, the rubble which remains of time, we discover such a chaos of conflicting data that we cannot conclude anything with certainty. The Uffington Horse is no horse at all, or perhaps more accurately, it is a horse only insofar as it is also concurrently everything else we can make of it. And we make this conclusion merely at this non-existent point of now, the Euclidean present. To take the issue across time, the possibilities complexify to another power with each new point of view we add to our investigations, until chaos engulfs all time and we must make meaning – any meaning possible – in order simply to survive.

And so, a little past four in the morning, having achieved no firm knowledge as regards the white horses of England, I shut down my laptop and understood that this work of trying to make the signs line up and behave was no less a pathological compulsion than the one which had engulfed my brother. It may be that I had laid off trying to force the data to comport with what I wanted it to, but I was by no means finished. Lying there as the dawn crawled up to meet me, I could only think about how I would subdue the information one day. All attempts to order information exhibit such neurosis, and that, devoid of play, the whole sordid process, although exhilarating during its undertaking, in the end yields only a barren, joyless, empty plain upon which the mind is then compelled to make its habitation.

But we can't stop ourselves.

*

Rising in the morning like a dying thing, I cleaned and packed up the little house at Woodhay, locked all the windows and doors and took the bus into Newbury. For my journey I brought the Plenderleath book, which I thought my friends would not miss, and, moving on from my investigations into the true status of the Uffington white horse – for now, at least – I checked on my phone for developments in the study of England's hill figures in the century and a half since Plenderleath had written his book, and I went over in my mind the shape of things as regarded the significance of these white horses.

When Plenderleath first moved to Cherhill – a little village only thirty miles west of where I had been staying that summer – and made his rounds visiting parishioners, he saw daily thrust up into the sky from the Downs to the south-east the recently erected Lansdowne monument, a stone obelisk nearly forty metres tall commissioned by the 3rd Marquis of Lansdowne in memory of Sir William Petty – not his own father, who, though a former prime minister, occupying that office during the last American war, was, except for in respect of his bitter and sarcastic turn of mind, largely forgotten even during his own lifetime; but rather his great-great-grandfather, the economist, physician, philosopher and scientist, and co-founder of the Royal Society. Commemoration, therefore, was for Plenderleath, so to speak, in the air. However, it was the white horse hill figure cut into Cherhill Down a little to the north to which Plenderleath's eye was drawn as he conducted his daily rounds. Soon after his arrival, he began researching the origins of this white horse, though it was not until twelve years later that he published his first work on the geoglyphs, 'On the White Horses of Wiltshire and its Neighbourhood', in 1872. Another twelve years hence, Plenderleath was busy preparing the full-length study of the phenomenon of these hill figures out of a quarter century of detailed notes, and yet this astute and sensitive reader of signs – archaeological, literary, interpersonal – was unable to see from his immersion in his own time that his was a rearguard action, that his very interest, in being a nostalgio-archaeological one, was symptomatic of a cultural death – it is only when we are threatened with separation from something that we find it necessary to keep it close – and that the inestimable complex which made up the culture of the people who lived around him had moved through this interest and now left it behind like a midden. We need look no further than to the two decades between the last scouring of the Uffington Horse in 1857 and the year of Plenderleath's first published study to see how the horse was being forgotten, and as a result disappearing back into the landscape, receding beneath the turf. By the time he wrote his last word on the matter, the horse had been allowed to sink into a lamentable state, one he himself describes as 'now so overgrown with weeds as scarcely to be discernable from a distance, except by a person who knows where to look for it'. Plenderleath stands at that moment when what is neglected must be restored, because everything else which was great, good and true – God, empire, status – is gradually being revealed to be a chimera, or worse.

All of the white horses of his studies, with the Uffington and original Westbury horses being two notably genuine ancient exceptions, had been cut in the preceding hundred years, and the last of these was cut in the same year as the Uffington was last cleaned. Over a person's lifetime, then, a fashion had arisen and then ebbed away, leaving straggly old nags and sometimes merely the ghost of a horse, one whose traces were only visible in the driest seasons, when the soil could be seen beneath the shrivelled grass, and the shape of which could rather be detected than seen, with the eye averted instead of trained directly upon the object of its inquiry. Now, online, one can find catalogues listing all the hill figures of Britain, including those figures which, by their neglect, are in the process of being irremediably lost. It is difficult not to wonder, for the items listed as vanishing or lost already, how it can be known, and whether they ever existed at all. Further, how many have been fully lost without our knowledge of their ever having existed?

If one walks over Gibbet Hill, for instance, one can look across the South Downs at Hindhead Common and see only scrub, the odd larch and the occasional straggly remnants of the ancient oak forest which had spread across the county before such a thing had been conceived. There, one can look directly upon the hill and be entirely oblivious to the presence, beneath a stand of several pine, of an old white horse, constructed at some point not long before 1913 out of stones gathered locally by Dr Oliver Gray and his family, after a design by E. A. Walton from Edinburgh. This horse, the catalogue records, has now been so choked with grass and weeds that it is no longer visible. Or the Rockley Horse, several miles north-west of Marlborough, which vanished long ago and was first suspected to be lying dormant beneath the ground when local shepherds, some time after the end of the Second World War, remarked upon the peculiarly discoloured turf over the crest of the Down. When the field draped over that hill was ploughed shortly afterwards, a great prancing white horse over one hundred and twenty-five feet long and sixty-six feet from back to toe was discovered to reside beneath, true to the prestidigitation of these powerless rustics. The horse's location, at the summit of a hill, perplexed then and perplexes still the expert and general observer alike, for it was and is scarcely visible from any vantage point in the vicinity, and could only ever have been seen from above, a perspective from which, at the presumed time of the horse's design and manufacture in the late eighteenth century, no human had ever been capable of achieving. (Wishing to be assured of the veracity of this assertion, I looked up hot-air ballooning, and discovered that my statement was true, excepting a select number of balloon enthusiasts in France, beginning with Pilâtre de Rozier and his friend and patron the Marquis François Laurent le Vieux d'Arlandes. He after great and careful experimentation with tethers to the ground and ballast both inanimate and animate – I noted with pleasure that the first creature to fly in a hot-air balloon was a particularly docile local goat – finally gained the honour of making the first untethered voyage into the air. Louis XVI attempted to heap this honour as punishment on convicted criminals, thus revealing (in one of those details of behaviour in which William Plenderleath delighted so much) that it is a greater terror by far than being imprisoned, or even perhaps than death – which however we must admit amounts to the same thing – to be utterly free of the earth.)

If we choose to focus merely on the horses (leaving aside all the human figures, giants, ears of corn, crosses, arrows and dogs – not to mention the abstract designs cut into the ground to aid the navigation of aircraft), there are sufficient numbers of these equestrian figures which have been found and then lost again, sinking back into the earth, to make one question what it is one walks upon in the day and sleeps above at night. Without regular maintenance and cleaning, the old horse at Devizes, originally made by local shoemakers at Whitsuntide in 1845, had already sunk back into the ground by the early 1920s, the only trace of its former presence being a discoloration to the grass at times of drought. In the remarkably arid summer of 1954, the head boy of the local grammar school while out cycling noticed the faint outline of a horse's head on the steep west side of Roundway Hill. Curious, he noted that this shape was only visible by looking away from it. 'If I looked intently at the hillside,' he wrote, 'what had maintained shape sank into shapelessness. But to look askance, that was when the distinctive profile of the horse presented itself to me, as if it were a timid creature which would only come out of the earth for the gentle and patient among us.' This and further contemporary observations formed the basis for a reconstruction of the horse, though at a new site so as not to cause distress to the horse which it was clear sought still to continue its slumber beneath this particular soil at that particular point of the hill. A generation later, with the horse no doubt having sunk deeper and closer toward oneness with the earth around it, happenstance again brought it out into the visible world, this time in the winter: a flash of lightning revealed, like an infrared imaging device, a differential dusting of snow upon the hillside, fine and finer, and the head reared up once again doubly out of the darkness of night and of deep time. Perhaps it will return to us, to our world, again, the enthusiasts say to one another, but they will not disturb it.

Just as the horse at Devizes has now sunk back into the ground, so it had been with the five red horses of Tysoe (at least one of which was intentionally destroyed), the Inkpen Horse, the Littlington Horse, the Pewsey Horse (which sank into the ground when, not long after it was first made in the late eighteenth century, the landowner, disliking the festivities, forbade the scouring which all the white horses require, and which was invariably attended by bouts of drinking and merrymaking), the Pitstone Hill Horse (the only record of which survives in a clutch of court and topographical documents from the early nineteenth century; no trace of the horse can be discovered today). All have gone. But who can say that some undreamed-of combination of light, drought or deluge, atmospheric humidity, soil acidity, and the curiosity of a human eye which likes to see without looking, loving the indirect approach to a thing as more subtle still, may bring these absent bodies back into themselves some time hence?

As the train took me across the fields of southern England I looked out at the hills as we passed, and I wondered how many had once been dressed with one of these lost horses, somehow there and not there, invisible yet extant, much like the river Bytham which was erased from existence half a billion years ago but whose channels must be evident down there beneath the ground still. I thought about the Uffington White Horse, a protected monument, one whose disappearance is, for the time being, deferred by the work of English Heritage in bestowing an annual scrubbing day upon it undertaken by volunteers. The continuity of this form on the hillside is assured, but only until the next cultural cataclysm, or merely a fading of interest or evaporation of funding. After I had returned home from Woodhay that day, I sat in my chair upstairs by the old sash window, observing the lines of the terraced roofs wind up the hill and my thoughts emerge and sink within my consciousness, and I was struck by the possibility that this particular figure at Uffington, the oldest surviving one we have, may not have had an uninterrupted existence. I recalled that Plenderleath makes quizzical reference to the absence of any mention of the White Horse of Uffington in any of the medieval topographers' studies of the local area excepting that in the eleventh-century cartulary of Abingdon Abbey. In this compilation of manuscripts we find the earliest record of the Uffington horse, if only obliquely, for the hill is referred to as 'white horse hill' (*mons albi equi*). Three centuries after this, in the next surviving mention of the horse, the author of *Llyfr Coch Hergest* wrote: 'Near to the town of

Abinton there is a mountain with a figure of a stallion upon it and it is white. Nothing grows upon it.' (*Gerllaw tref Abinton y mae mynydd ac eilun march arno a gwyn ydiw. Ni thyf dim arno.*) Working from this evidence, Plenderleath suggests that the horse, in a reference to the standard of Hengist, meaning 'stone horse' in Saxon, was dug from the ground by King Alfred's forces in order to commemorate their victory over the Danes at nearby Reading. The absence of any reference to the horse in the earlier literature of Britain – in Tacitus, Dio Cassius, Gildas, Bede, Nennius, or Geoffrey of Monmouth – led Plenderleath to the conclusion that the Uffington White Horse is 1,200 years old. Knowing, however, from silt dating carried out in the 1990s that the figure is in fact vastly older – around three thousand years old – could it not be possible that this great monument, one which appears to have survived all the vicissitudes of time, and more impressively, in appearing, without coordination, without continuous welfare or systematic attention, to have been cleaned every seven years or so from the Bronze Age up until the present day, against all that we know of the fashions and fads of humankind – is it not possible, in fact probable, that the Uffington Horse sank into oblivion some time before writing emerged, before the Romans came, and was rediscovered a millennium later, perhaps during a period of drought, or when the lightning and the snow saw fit to reveal it to a wandering eye? There is no mention in any of the earlier sources because it could not be seen, though it was still there, hidden. And so, is it not possible, as the emergence of Plenderleath's voice from this deadwood page seems also to assert, against all propriety of reason, that such things that are lost forever might not be lost at all, and that everything which dies is somehow still there, if only we could obtain to the means of its retrieval? That the dead, in short, do not need to answer our questions because they are not really dead, merely under a different form or species of matter.

TREE

On one particular day it was decided that we – a close friend and I – would visit the memorial which had been made to the German writer W. G. Sebald in the grounds of the University of East Anglia, where he had worked until his death. We did not know where the memorial was, but it appeared impossible, despite the significant size of the campus, that we should not find it.

My companion, being an alumna of the university, knew into her feeling the rabbit-cropped grass of the slopes to the east, the deciduous woods to the south-west, the duckboards and weed around the lake, the gravel at its shore, the arced bridge, foxgloves, substation, winding paths, the pipework, service roads and steam of the realm beneath the surface of the university where the students walked the walkways and the light made stark the angles of its brutalist architecture. For me, it was just another place. As we walked along the path around the lake we came upon the astonishing sight of the ziggurats, the stepped pyramids of the halls of residence which looked so misplaced at the top of the fields above the water's edge, as if the remains of an Aztec civilisation had been discovered in Norfolk. It was better, I was told, not to look at any one of these singly but to step back in sight so to speak and see them all, together, as a composite, because that is how they look best. Also (said as an aside) pass over the concrete, steel and glass of their manufacture, which once seen entirely ruin the illusion.

We passed between the ziggurats and under the library, went up staircases and over walkways, down into pipe-embroidered tunnels, unlit cubbies, across gardens, round the backs of the lecture halls and teaching rooms, past pieces of modernist statuary, down through the drifts of fallen leaves where the pump station thrums – but nowhere could we find anything like a memorial. We redoubled our efforts, but only managed to measure by our increasing familiarity with the forgotten regions of this expanse of humanised space a growing sense of how lost at our task we were. Dead ends, backtrackings and general consternation frustrated us continually. I was struck by the absurd vision of W. G. Sebald riding off on the Uffington White Horse, neither of them ever to be found again.

In the original German (so my companion, an Austrian by birth, informed me), Sebald's sentences are great baroque structures which seem never to wish to reach an end. Winding down and over the pages to terminate at one mysterious and singular point after another, it is as if each were part of a battalion of discourse compelled to parachute element-by-element from a plane so high overhead as to be inaudible, even unseen, and swing slowly down in mysterious loops through the air. In the English translations which have been made of his work, by contrast, Sebald's voice is often dealt to the reader in a rapid staccato, short bursts of image. It struck me as odd, as we continued to walk on in silence, that our language, which in so many ways is so close to its sibling German, should require such extreme reconfiguration.

I thought again – and again with that inescapable sorrow which overcomes me at these strange moments when I consider the artefacts and instruments of a culture recent enough to appear familiar, but ones which our own has so comprehensively superseded in its technological development as to make them appear quaint and simple – I thought again of the pink upon the maps of Europe which had been used for both Britain and Germany by the German and Scottish cartographers as a gesture of a common fealty in their ideals; cartographers who themselves had shared resources and information with one another, but who had by the drift of history into war been forced to alter and rewrite this brotherhood, recasting this shared heritage as something which never was and never would be again, the tint within the two separate countries becoming gradually differentiated until there was no possibility of doubt that they were different colours and nothing held them in common. Perhaps, it occurred to me, there was only true, sustainable peace down under the sea, away from all humans, on the plains of Doggerland, where there could be no need for talk or language. After several hours of wandering through the vast expanse which we had made of our search through those three hundred acres we abandoned the attempt and returned to our separate homes.

This search lay forgotten for several months until, following a chance mention of Sebald on the radio, or perhaps it was in an overheard conversation, I was reminded of our failed mission and idly began searching again – not this time for the memorial itself, which I was persuaded by the comprehensiveness of our exploration could not exist, but rather for the source of our misinformation. I began with the Wikipedia entry for Sebald, and then branched out to wherever the consequent links might take me. I tunnelled and burrowed all around the figure of W. G. Sebald, through masses of information of varying densities, down, across, through all the discontinuous strata of data, but still I could find no mention made of any memorial to the writer, whether on the grounds of UEA campus or not. It seemed impossible that we had entirely invented the memorial, and yet this was the only explanation I could arrive at. I messaged my friend, who almost immediately messaged back that she had found the source. Choosing uncharacteristically to read in her native language, which she claims to dislike, my friend discovered from the German Wikipedia entry on Sebald what it was we had been looking for. After a brief description of his upbringing in Bavaria (I summarise from the translation she made for me down the phone), his father's post-war imprisonment as a captain in the Wehrmacht, his studies in Germany and Switzerland, then his eventual move to England – and immediately following a summary discussion of his works, a bibliography and a list of awards – there was a brief notice of two *Gedenkstätten*, or memorials: first, *Sebaldweg*, a walk officially designated to the writer's memory by Wertach municipality where the writer lived as a child, a walk which he describes taking in *Vertigo* and which now features six steles engraved with text from this passage of the novel mounted in concrete to the side of the path; and second, that which we had been seeking, the reference to Sebald Copse, located on the grounds of the University of East Anglia. It was described as being a copper beech tree (*Blutbuche*, literally 'blood beech') planted by his family and enclosed within a bench of wooden rings engraved with a quotation from a piece of Sebald's verse which gives the title to his and his close friend Jan Peter Tripp's collaborative project *Unerzählt*: 'Unerzählt / bleibt die Geschichte / der abgewandten / Gesichter', which has been translated by Michael Hamburger as 'Untold remain the stories of the averted faces.' There followed, as if in anticipation of our doubts, a photograph of the ringed bench beneath this description.

And so, while this discovery revived our quest to locate the memorial, which it seemed most definitely did exist; and while we felt the very useful marker for its location – the distinctive foliage of the copper beech – was sure to assist us; no amount of searching, once we had returned to the campus, led us anywhere closer to the discovery of this ring of seats with the words of the poet carved into them. It was at this point that it occurred to me that W. G. Sebald, whose preoccupation with memorialisation, absences, obliteration, confusion, labyrinths, and so on is unmistakable throughout his work, would have surely appreciated the grotesque irony of these two humans seeking out and failing to find a memorial to himself. We checked all the necessary data: the proper botanical translation of the term '*Blutbuche*', the seasonal appearance of the copper beech (following the confirmation of this species as the one in question), an estimate of the size of the tree, taking into account the species' growth rate and the passage of fifteen years. And yet, around none of the half dozen copper beech trees that we found, did we find in turn what we were really seeking.

Some weeks later, or perhaps it was longer, I chanced while browsing for information about trees – I forget what it was I was seeking this time – upon a number of reproductions of photographs from the latter nineteenth century up to the present day recording instances in which trees had grown around what had been attached to or leant up against them, in some cases entirely swallowing the object in question. There were numerous examples of signs nailed to trees being grown about with swellings of the bark, which resembled great folds of fat, and sucked into the oblivion which resides beneath the surface of the tree. In one photograph, railings originally erected in a circle around a plane tree to protect it have been outgrown, subsumed by its dappled flanks, so that, where portions of it are still visible, the wrought iron appears to be growing out of the tree itself, as if some kind of monstrous excrescence, an error in the code of nature; or perhaps as a retaliation, in which nature fights back against genetic modification and begins to grow imitations of the man-made from out of itself, becoming half machine. Mostly though the effect was of consumption. Numerous bicycles, presumably leant against trees at some point long past and for some unknowable reason never retrieved, are identifiable by the exhibition of handlebars or portions of wheel in protrusions from the bark of elms, oaks, beeches and larch. In one remarkable case in Connecticut, the upper portion of the gravestone of one Samuel St John sticks out of a crease in the trunk of a large horse chestnut, with only the legend 'Here lies the Remains of Mr Samuel St John… His Life…' and the date '1779' remaining open to the air.

Since this second failed expedition, I sometimes go and sit in the little disordered park around the corner and look at the woodland receding into the distance within itself, and I wonder what of man might have been swallowed up by that wood, and what happens to all the flesh – and the metals and stones and plastics of the objects which we make and carry – following their entombment in these fibrous grave markers. And inevitably I then think again of the memorial to W. G. Sebald, and it occurs to me with complete certainty that the ringed bench carrying those sorrowful words had, despite being wood itself, been swallowed into the body of the copper beach as it grew, and that this perhaps was the only means of the preservation of the writing which had been carved into its surface, because everything which maintains contact with the air, while visible, must inevitably perish. That which is buried, lost to air and sight, is turning, turning into something else, making growth towards another instantiation, and everything is its own seed and has its own will, just as in the case of Artyom Sidorkin, from Izhevsk in the Urals, in whose lung there was found a living fir tree; or the peculiar case of Carl Leche who, studying the Mkodos tribe and their habitat in Madagascar in the 1870s, saw with his own eyes a woman who, after drinking the nectar-like juice which was held in a bowl structure within the crotch of a tree, fell into a stupor, and the eight branches of the tree, which had lain dormant across the jungle floor, rose, wrapped the woman up tightly, and dragged her down into its core, where she was consumed.

Now, whenever I find myself out there in the woods, I am invariably led to a contemplation of the limitless possibility of trees. I cannot but find myself considering King Charles sheltered within the crotch of an oak, nor the public house which had been opened up within the hollow of a yew tree in Sussex, nor that other ancient carbuncled yew in Crowhurst, Surrey in which was found, upon local residents deciding to cut a hole and furnish it with a door, a cannonball from the civil war buried in its interior. Nor can I suppress the wilful belief that somewhere there stands a mature tree containing an entire human body within it, that such a thing cannot be but inevitable in consideration of their closeness, not forgetting that humans can be foster parents of trees within such inhospitable habitats as their lungs, or can be born containing other humans within their infant selves, and that these may grow and kill their host and so themselves, and who may there be to remember these poor unknown and missing ones, trees and people alike?

Trees seem so to shriek out the anguish of their predicament that who can say that they weren't human in one form or another prior to this sedentary existence? When I think of trees, I think of 'Odin's Rune Song' from the Hávamál:

I know that I hung on a windy tree, nine long nights,
wounded with a spear, dedicated to Odin,
myself to myself,
on that tree of which no man knows from where its roots run.

And when I think of Odin I think of you, because there was no escape from the horror of signs as they overwhelmed you both.

No bread did they give me nor a drink from a horn,
downwards I peered;
I took up the runes,
screaming I took them,
then I fell back from there.

It was in the evening of the same day – that day on which we hadn't discovered Sebald's memorial for the second time – that I experienced the sudden conception that you would come to the door and announce by your simple presence there a continued living, that the tree had not got you, and this conception was appalling not because of the deceit which would have been involved, nor the subtlety of the trick, but because you most certainly should be dead: that neither of us wanted you to be alive.

★

Again I decided I would go out and find the tree, but only in thought can I do so. In body I am like that tree which took you.

In thought, I cross the bare raked fields of the county behind a long window and rock to the movement of the train; or else I walk or ride. How would I know it when I came to be there? Often I have imagined when out walking along the edges of corn- or barley fields looking past the outer spread of the hawthorn or whitethorn into and through the dark interior down to a ditch and there seeing a human body. If asked to cut down a dead and hanging human, I would seek under force of fear to make the cut to the twine as far from the neck and head as possible, which would be the part looped around the bough, and so the twine would drop too, and no trace be left. Or would this not occur to me? Would I be brought to dwell by the violent singularity of its achievement on the straight tension of the note-taut string between these two beings, not considering the loop, and cut there? I cannot say. Would he who cut down your body have cut at the bough or the free thread? How else am I to know your tree without the twine noosed about it there in a sign? And yet somehow I know I will already know it, by what it, itself, has known.

★

Yes, often I take myself there to that little patch of woodland, by where the river draws the border between Essex and Suffolk, but he is never there. Now I think about it, the woodland I go to during those journeys – journeys without duration, instantaneous transportations – is not here (or there) at all, but a place where we used to play when everything was strange, which is how the world is for little people of ten years old who are told they know nothing but live more in truth than any adult.

Intoxicated at that age by a newly acquired freedom to roam, every field boundary was a frontier. Closer to civilisation, at the end of my friend's enormous garden – so enormous that it morphed into woodland and no one knew where it ended – there was an area of the woods beneath where the common field sloped down that we particularly preferred. We had a name for it, certainly not a very good one, but I can't remember it – The Pit, perhaps. There, one night when a friend and I camped out beside the fire in just sleeping bags, a bobbled glass bottle of Corona orangeade which we had half-drunk – I remember these bobbled bottles perfectly, the brand holding an aura of distinction for me – exploded from overheating by its close proximity to the fire, and the cap and a ring of glass caught within it fired like a gunshot between our heads and through the dark nettles beyond the cast of firelight at terrific speed. This woodland, where we had spent so much time as children, some thirty miles from the place where my brother killed himself, is indefatigable in asserting itself across that space, against the logic of time also, and becoming the place I visit where he last was, which is where he wasn't. Places, for we feelingful humans, are like pools which may be stepped into from decades hence, causing shimmers and shakes at their surface and turnings in their body beneath, and most curiously which cause those held in the hollows of other times to shimmer and shake in echo.

Every tree is capable of becoming his – yours. I know the tree, and sometimes I look up and see the orange nylon cord which still hangs there – the cord which was used to tie the haystacks when we were young, and which I thought was no longer in use.

Evidence given at the inquest and contained in the coroner's report is clear about the orange nylon, or at least I think it is – still I have not read this document, nor will I ever, but go only on hearsay. I remember a conversation on the phone with our mother, who told me about it, but perhaps I invented the cord as another link with the past. (Is perhaps the difference between art and madness the difference between making and seeing order in disorder?) I know the tree, and sometimes the cord is there; the wood is deciduous, and the light is springbright, with the dapple of the shadows of leaves shivering over the trunks as the wind moves. The smell is of damp but fresh earth, as if it were recently turned, though of course it cannot have been because it is in the depths of woodland. At these times I go to the woods because it is the most peaceful place I can find, something I do not understand, because my brother's last moments were only brutal.

At other times, though more rarely, I enter into those last moments. The wood disappears, there is only a body, or rather only the holes opened into the body, and there is only feeling. It is a very difficult sensation to give account of – it moves along the fuzzy boundary between physical and emotional pain, or perhaps knits them together, makes me aware that they are less different than we would commonly believe.

If I see a body, it is only a glance through the porthole of a door – the door to the mortuary, perhaps – and then the door swings open and I must turn away for fear of seeing. At such times as I have these visions I am neither asleep nor awake, but something entirely different, immersed in a world of repetitions, emblems, feelings for symbols which are flooded with colour and light. It is neither pleasant nor unpleasant, but it is necessary. Visiting and seeing that rigid, twisted body is not something I want to do, nor is it something which I feel would be helpful in any way. Looking is an unnecessary act, though in the facticity of a body – these things were inflicted upon a body I knew *by* that body, *making* that body – I am inevitably drawn there despite all this, just as we read of the deaths of hundreds without feeling very much at all, except perhaps a rush of numbers, as if we were addicted to hearing of death, more and bigger death, year upon year, because we are conditioned to appreciate a sense of *progress*.

More than once it has been said by people I talk to that what you did to yourself put them in mind of the Crucifixion, which fits, I suppose. Certainly the Cross has always been called also a tree – most spectacularly in the Dream of the Rood, where the vision of a tree dressed in gold and jewels floats in the air before the narrator, bleeding from its right side. It begins to speak, and tells of what happened, how it was cut down by its enemies in order to be mounted upon a hill and have a criminal hung off it. When it sees Christ come up the hill and climb willingly up to be nailed to its crossbeams, the tree is filled with wonder, and it sings out at the moment of their being nailed together as one:

þurhdrifan hi me mid deorcan næglum. On me syndon þa
   dolg gesiene,
opene inwidhlemmas. Ne dorste ic hira nænigum sceððan.
Bysmeredon hie unc butu ætgædere. Eall ic wæs mid blode
   bestemed,
begoten of þæs guman sidan, siððan he hæfde his gast onsended.

They skewered me with dark nails, wounds easily seen upon me,
treacherous strokes yawning open. I dared injure none of them.
They shamed us both together. I was besplattered with blood,
sluicing out from the man's side, after launching forth his soul.

★

It will come as no surprise to discover, in leafing though the first volume of Robert Chambers' *Book of Days*, published in 1864, that, on that same day of your death, Machiavelli – he who has given his surname to political skulduggery and his forename, as Old Nick, to the devil – was born. I do not mean that you died in 1469, but it is a meaningful correspondence nevertheless.

Meaningful too, in some fine and irretrievable sense, is that connection we find between the main article of this day – 3 May – and this, your tree, your vanishing act, your attempt to escape the insupportable work of signs, work which is occurring now in me.

Chambers, who had in a previous work roughly anticipated Darwin's theory of evolution, entitles the article 'Invention (or discovery) of the Holy Cross', and proceeds to give a humorous account – humorous in order to be dismissive – of the miraculous properties of the Cross. Which is to say, in truth, an account of the miraculous properties of that human organ of thought which may convince itself of its own logic while upholding the most preposterous fallacies as fact. Chambers recounts how the Empress Helena, mother of Constantine and early saint of the two Churches, discovered the One True Cross among many others when on tour in Jerusalem, after a dead man was placed on its branches and it exhibited the property of bringing him back to life. Although this cross was placed in the custody of the Bishop of Jerusalem, it immediately began to grow smaller in the loss of those parts of itself requested by fervent pilgrims at the conclusion of their travels to that city. Little by little, with all these wedges being cut from it, we might imagine the cross would have been consumed and disappeared into nothing but a dispersal of splinters – except that it was found, so Chambers reminds us, that the wood of the cross possessed the power of reproducing itself, and that, howsoevermuch was cut off, the substance could not be diminished. Well over a millennium later, after the cross had travelled into Persia and back, thus forming the tradition of Holyrood Day, and at least one of the four nails which had once been driven through the Son of God into its beams had been placed by St Helena in the iron crown of Lombardy, later brought into France by Charlemagne, or thrown into the Adriatic in order to quell it, John Calvin wrote a pamphlet, translated into English by Stephen Wythers and published in 1561, dealing with the fashion for relics. The fad had risen from the time of Helena through the medieval period to become, literally, a matter of life and death. For a thousand years, all across medieval Europe, the laity would pay vast quantities of money to be buried within the main bodies of the churches, close by where the relics were held, for this was conceived to be a primary source of these buildings' sanctity; the cemetery, by contrast, was for the abandoned poor, who were buried in mass graves of about six hundred bodies before being covered over. Chambers writes that Calvin – or Calvyne, as his name is represented therein – states via his translator that 'so great a quantity of fragments of the true cross were scattered among the Christian churches in his time, that they would load a large ship; and that, whereas the original cross could be carried by one man, it would take three hundred men to support the weight of the existing fragments of it.' Chambers goes on to give Calvin's account of all the other relics which Christ handled or touched and their location in the reformist theologian's day, including the numerous nails (far more than the original four), the spear which pierced his side (now numbering at least seven, for this was the number of places in which the spear could now be found), the crown of thorns (recently saved in our own time from the electrical fire which destroyed the roof of Notre Dame cathedral in Paris), the manger in which he had lain, the swaddling bands in which he had been wrapped, his cradle, and the shirt his mother had made for him out of the finest Egyptian cotton. Pieces of bread and fish, the paschal knife, a platter, numerous cloths, a palm branch and a crumbling of earth – taken from that place where He had stood when raising Lazarus from the dead – are also identified by Calvyne, so Chambers tells us, as relics still to be found about us in the churches of Europe. Henry Stephens, writing in the middle of the sixteenth century, so Chambers continues, identifies the location in the most hallowed spaces of several French churches of Christ's blood, tears and even a portion of his breath. Chambers goes on to ridicule the assertion of the Church that for many of the martyrs, a single body part might be found in more than one place, forgetting, we must presume, when dismissing the idea that a foot of St Philip's could be found in three different places, that he, Chambers himself, was born with six fingers on each hand and six toes on each foot, an abnormality which, by his mother's commitment to correcting it, had left him lame, though at times he could clearly still feel their presence there at his extremities. Immediately preceding his concluding remarks, Chambers pokes fun at one particular relic-monger whom he describes exhibiting a feather of the Holy Ghost, 'supposing, no doubt, from the pictorial representations, that the sacred spirit was a real pigeon'.

Chambers' concluding remarks deserve to be quoted in full: 'There is an old story of a rather sceptical visitor of sacred places in France, in the earlier part of the sixteenth century, to whom in a certain monastery the skull of John the Baptist was shown, on which he remarked, with some surprise, "Ah! The monks of such-and-such a monastery also showed me the skull of John the Baptist yesterday." "True," said the monastic exhibitor, not disconcerted, "but those monks only possess the skull of the saint when he was a young man, and ours was his skull when advanced in years and wisdom."'

*

When it happens that the day has become the third of May again – and even when it is not, it may be: whether in spring or autumn, or deep in the winter, early or late in whichever month it happens to be, it is always possible that I am there, at the third day of May again – I find myself drawn again to the places, the nodes of the world in which information or feeling resides. I cannot bring myself to read the coroner's report; I cannot go to the clearing in which the deed was done – and it is not *cannot* so much as *must not*: to do so would be to attenuate what is well-jointed, square, plumb, straight and true, a thing constructed in me like a good handmade chair or table, perfect in its form.

I do like to drive and then stop, as the liking takes me, to enter into the interiors of the old rural East Anglian churches. Funny that this was what we had been forced to do as children, we – the children – bellowing our opposition to going in yet another stupid church, and now here I am doing it on my own.

Just last week I entered the church at Houghton-on-the-Hill to discover the warden preparing the place for a coming service. When we fell into talking, I must have mentioned Chambers' takedown of the relic tradition with his mirthful rhetoric, because the warden told me that it was hardly surprising that the relics exhibited such properties, being as they were, first and foremost, signs. She continued to say that a sign is a thing which, though certainly physical, has no limit to its signification; and thus that Chambers might be as wrong as he was right. Out in the grounds, as we trod over the dampwarm grass between the buttercups and daisies, the warden told me of a conversation she had once had with an arborist who lived in the village, and who had been brought in by an association of local parish councils following the 1986 storms to manage the clearing of unstable trees on Church land, in which he had said without irony that, if certain plants have been found to reproduce alone, and money can be said to propagate itself when in the right hands, then why shouldn't it be discovered one day that anything might be capable of giving rise to itself, and becoming multiple, even ourselves? Several years later, this arborist, so the church warden told me, had an accident while working at West Stow Country Park in the woods around Beeches Pit which ended his career and left him in permanent pain. After this, he developed a serious addiction first to prescription painkillers, and then to gambling, and disappeared. Every year, on the day that he took his own life, the church warden told me, she could not help sensing this man, not in memory, which she was at pains to emphasise was not at all what she meant, but as a real presence there in the trees which he had pollarded, cutting them down low so as to save them.

Everywhere, echoes.

★

From the very beginning, the tree is inescapable. Look at it! Busy working its way into itself, boughs and foliage, in search of that leap to double itself and become symbol. Every tree dead at its centre so as to make a space there for that later turning-in.

The frame of every house formed from its timbers, the furze upon the roofs, the wheels of the wagons which the horse draws forth. Culinary implements, the fuel over which to cook, the nuts and fruits and berries we eat. If one stands in the late light to look upon an expanse of still water, and there within the lapping stands a tree, it is doubled at its trunk, up and down; as it is in the air, so it is beneath the earth in its rooten self, as the picture in the water makes visible. So then, too, in time, to take each self, every person, I, you, he, she, that living reality at the very base of the trunk, dwelling at that shimmering line which is called present, and below are all those who made possible the trunkself, and above are all those who the trunkself will makebecome. To conceive of this intersection, isn't it monstrous? You are just a little knot in time, but upon which so much of flesh hangs. Is it not divine?

Family trees are very sensible devices, and yet they are not at all as they appear. Or the true state of things is not as the family tree would have us believe. Do not forget that a tree stands in at least three dimensions! We people think that everything is laid out flat and well formed, no knots or hollows, no hunch, lurch, contortion or twist, but that is not how time works on trees, or families either. Every bud is root-tip too. Everywhere is somewhere else, doubled, squared, cubed, more. Nothing can be grasped but it grows again beyond.

Is this you speaking now, or I?

It cannot be told.

In truth, the trunk of the tree penetrates the rock of earth and plunges down, not branching out but forcing its way down like a rock drill through the earth's crust, down into the mantle, exploring the liquid rock, down through the silicate slop to where the molten iron is, until it reaches the very centre, the ferrous core, and at the centre of the centre, what is there? Did you not know that all of this came forth simply from a gathering of dust? What is there at the centre of things except nothing at all? A minuscule point, a vanishment. Repeat a word after me – tree – and what do you have in the end, at the centre, except a vanishment?

I had to tie one end of the twine to a stick so that I could throw it over the bough up above me and draw down its end to make the knot. There is a pragmatics even to self-slaughter.

There are so many infinitesimal stages to a given act that to describe them all in the absolute detail of their instantiation would fill a whole universe with words. What a joy it would be to fill a whole universe with words!

When one makes a knot, a little bow in twine, doesn't it recall all those other times, which in their turn recall that first and primary time, one knee hard down on the floor, the foot behind become paddle pressed down to the ground, rudder, the other face up and beaming with the bend of itself – a knee you will notice does smile in its bending – back curved over, head hung in concentration over the working fingers which won't work so damn it, how is it so hard to learn to tie the laces of your shoes? Cross, turn, loop under, draw, extend, make good tensile abutment up against the instep of the foot, and then the holding fingertip, and round and about it such loopings and turnings commence, so many movements that the universe is filling with words like the air of an estuary when the crack of a gunshot lifts all the impossible birds, and isn't it true that each person has a different method, one which they learned, passed down from parent to child, each idiosyncratic method repeated, doubled, into infinite iteration, the culture of the shoelace no different from any other, I suppose, though there's always a black sheep with bad boots on his hooves making forbidden differents in refusal of best good sense and kindly guidance.

(If I had to describe him in a single phrase, it would be: wilfully uncooperative.)

If you had said, Go kill yourself, like you wanted, then none of this would have happened.

(This proves my point.)

When I came about, there was a bright gathering of flames and a bursting forth; when you happened, there was a dull pat, and a thing rolled over in the grass, and didn't they all coo.

★

Sometimes I look down at the round earth as if from space, a reversal of what the Dreamer of the Rood saw, but still we look at the same: that tree which forms the axis on which the whole world turns. Contrary to the myth, the Great Wall of China can't be seen from up here without magnification, but I can see down to your tree in all its detail, how the leaves quiver, the buds waxy and reddening at their tips.

Sometimes, I open Google Maps and zoom out and in, seeking something, idly, not thinking it is you, knowing nothing can come of it but doing it nevertheless. Always I am drawn to Stoke-by-Clare and I see the river loop south under the village; I see the businesses and organisations labelled – Stoke College Preparatory School, Sheridan Sport Horses livery and stables, Stoke Stores. Unable to go there in person, I hover around in the air, move through the galaxy of images and words around the nexus where you burned yourself out. Here, on one particular occasion, I discover with excitement that there is graffiti extant on the walls and pillars of the church of St John the Baptist made by members of the congregation half a millennium ago. I feel compelled to follow these trails of forgotten people. What are we to do with those of whom such a little remains, a singular scrap or scratch, hardly a trace at all?

I feel compelled to bear witness, which is all anyone can do. All these traces so little, so fugitive, but exerting a gravitational force: irresistible, inescapable, life-sustaining.

Unlike the architecture of this and the other churches of the region, unlike the stained glass, the design of the pews, the details of the altar, the statues in the niches – all of which were under the control of the highest social class in the land – the inscriptions made in the stone of the church were made by everyone, ecclesia and laity, from the priests to the lords to the people who farmed the local land, tended livestock, tiled and thatched the roofs, fired and lay the bricks, felled, sawed and carpented the wood. Only three of the markings to the walls of the church at

Stoke-by-Clare are written, one a Latin inscription memorialising a cleric of the church who died on 15 April 1567, and the other two illegible scrawls, though perhaps names. In one of several portraits, a jester wears a hat with a bell; in another, a sorrowful face, half-formed, peers out of the stone as if trapped and desirous of emerging into true life in the cool quiet space of the church. In addition to portraits there are candles, animals, geometric designs and abstract figures. In one, the head of a dove emerges atop a tangle of striations, to the right of what is perhaps a crow, which itself could be above a sheep's head, the whole signed by

one Robert Reid. (Some of the shapes emerging out of the stone are like the clouds one looked at as a child, wherein we saw whatever we wanted to, the same clouds which, now we have become adults, do nothing for us.)

A recurring figure is an exceptionally perfect circle, divided by a number of curves having the same radius, to the formation of designs symmetrical across one or two axes. Why? What is it for? Who made it, and what was the force that drove them to undertake that making? How is the circle so perfect? The depiction of a braid whose three strands turn at right angles begins and ends nowhere, flowing out of and into the indeterminate rock. There is also an abstract motif which recalls four feet of a lion, or perhaps four bells of trumpets, whose legs, or bores, plait round each other three times, and which can mean nothing except that it recalls into the presence of the observer by the care of its making the patient consciousness of he or she who made it. The same is the case for a figure whose lines recall a human body with a spear through its midst, its arms raised in supplication or defence, and its head indicated by a cross whose stem runs down to form its body, as if it were the Cross become a man, taking on the injuries of Christ, except here fighting back against them. Or perhaps resisting the injuries He whom had been nailed to it by His own Godly necessity had sustained on Calvary. Perhaps this little carving in stone was made to avenge Him some 1,500 years after the fact in a little parish church on the Essex–Suffolk border a quarter of a mile from where my brother did that same number on himself.

Looking at this graffiti scratched into the pillars of a little church in Suffolk, I could not but be reminded of the famous Pompeiian graffiti, discovered in the eighteenth century, though so much older than that of the English churches. I began trawling through catalogues and transcriptions, and found them to be mostly declaring in words love for or insults against another. Their existence is astounding, but they remain almost exclusively bawdy and comic, and always in writing. By contrast, the individuals in Stoke-by-Clare who had made these inscriptions are both individual and whole – they are not reduced by the terms of their statement to occupying a genre of inscription writing – and in an instant they rushed up at me out of five hundred years of oblivion even with only a network of data and a computer monitor as intermediary. Words, in this instance, I found to have failed.

*

One day I left the house in a state of agitation, and it was only when I discovered myself quite by chance to have reached the gates of the crematorium that the source of that agitation revealed itself and the lie of chance was again unmasked. The long straight driveway brought me in a steady incline up to the chapel, while on either side the Victorian graves of the cemetery peeped through gaps in the hedge and building contractors smoked on the veranda of an old pavilion they were turning into a cafe. The last time

I had been here, it had been for the funeral of a friend's father, to which there came several hundred people, too many to fit with any due decorum in the chapel. In the end people clambered over one another, shared that close space about themselves normally reserved for themselves, and made particoloured celebration of a man who had never stopped talking, it seemed, from the day he had been born. A year or two prior to that the funeral was for Mark, and there were three of us living in attendance in that same room, which bellowed with the ignominy of its emptiness. Shame and a grand complex of suppression followed him up the chimney; and then we were out in the air again and it was over – or perhaps only beginning. I will say again that I stood at his wreathless name tag which queued on the slab outside and had an overwhelming urge to take off my shoes and leave them there for him, but I did not.

Revisiting this place alone, several years later, I went past the queue of wreaths, along a long rectangle of close-cropped lawn and out into the memorial gardens. Groundsmen were mowing the lawns and pruning the rose bushes. Here and there a family member knelt down at a plaque or stone and replenished flowers or made special spruce-up to edges and ledges. As I followed the paths deeper into the gardens of the crematorium, the memorials gathered in greater density until they appeared huddled in a silent crowd, as the living people inside the chapel gathered daily for their one who had died. Everywhere I looked the light was being treated to a great variety of colour and texture. Rockeries, ferns, smooth-cut marble, gold gilt, woodchip, water – all of them under the sun. I descended some steps to a grotto hollowed out of the earth. At its centre there was a rectangular recess holding the water of a pond. Delicate weed spread through the water and around a fountain which made a trickling whose sound was incomparably calming. I was here for no reason I could have accounted for; equally, I did not care to imagine any other place to be, so I stood above the bright green water of the pond and listened to its play. The dates engraved into the fascias of the stones ranged about were speckled across time. Many were from the preceding decade; some from a generation before; just a few were from the early part of the last century. I was struck momentarily by an image of time having to squeeze itself into space in this way, making steady endeavour to accommodate itself to the requirements of the people who are compelled to continue living within it, just as one can continually cut a straw in half and never reach its end. All these people who had lived, and what was left of them now – at least from my current vantage point, in this current state of mind – was far more powerful than any living being. When a thing becomes a sign, a little tear opens up at its centre, like a pip or gap of power. Even if beneath the smooth-faced stones there were ashes and charred nubs of bone, most of these people were out in the air, scattered across the fields, flowing in the rivers or drifting in the currents of the North Sea. It was not the ash or bone that mattered, nor the stone, nor the little rockery and ferns, but rather the making shape which was enabled by this little pip or opening in time. But what can be done if there is no pip or point, no tending place for a making to be made? It is unnatural. I come here with the trowel of my thought and feeling, and there is nothing and nowhere to dig or trim, and so all I can do is stare into a weak tinkling of water as if it were a blank cave wall before the conception of paint, and me not knowing how to become human.

Beyond, in the old cemetery, where the roots rear up beneath the paths and the squirrels perform their frantic work, the graves stand amid long pale grass and the soil is always a little damp and fragrant even in the height of summer. I was walking the looping paths in the knowledge that I would reach an exit from the place at some edge or other of its vast plot, though caring little which, when I reached the plot for the stillborn children. Here, the little graves are fenced and gated, stuck with gaudy windmills or animals on sticks, overseen by mass-produced cast cement angels and decorated with multicoloured plastic streamers. Despite this chintz, the overall effect of this little plot of a hundred graves is profoundly moving. Lives which never or hardly even began are brought together in a single gathered community. There is no shame here. I thought of my brother, how he had absconded, lived in the woods for nine days, hunted – or held himself to be hunted – until the course of his continued living was visible before him and it was deemed to be, in a word, unpalatable. And so he had finished himself from that tree, and then been brought here to be burned up several hundred feet away from these little children's bones. It struck me that when he had been burned he had lain upwards of the prevailing wind, and so hadn't he come to rest here also, upon and with these children? I wondered if this was something which might have comforted him in that final moment when the string sang out a true single-noted melody in its tautness. My brother did some terrible things, but always in the end I feel that he was an innocent.

Is it perhaps easier to die than ever to tend to the dead? Certainly it is easier than to tend to the dead who have no place, because where is the pip or point, the gap or space, the special place outside of time, for the tending to happen?

★

Again I found myself out in the woods to find the tree. The tree which is like every tree dead at its centre. To hit the tree with a heavy and hard object is to excite a resonance within the dead core of the tree which the particularities of its shape and specific cellulo-fibrous structure make peculiar to it. Every tree has its specific sound and sonority. It is perhaps a pollarded crack willow, but it cannot be: it must contend with light and shadow, inviolate be. It is perhaps a white willow or black poplar at the riverside, its trunk tigered by the sun and shadows as it glances from the face of the water. Could it be, a beech or larch or elm, the tree?

When I am there at its foot I am looking up and the branches divide above me like time, crossing with the tines and times of every other. There is only good clear clean light, deep dark creases, silvergreen bark. Only is there: silence. What sound could be made by a body at its death there hanging from the tree? It should not, never be, but it is, and done.

To push on in life, to live there, at the edge of sense, continually – is that possible? Can a body and a mind tolerate exile there at the hinterland of what is human? Or is this the only existence which there is, always-exile?

★

Hollows in trees are commonly begun by injury – a wind-felled limb or lightning strike. When the sapwood is revealed to the air, the tree becomes susceptible to microbial or animal attack. Beetles, fungi and bacteria are capable of hollowing out a tree to its very heartwood; though to create a space in which a vertebrate may dwell can take several centuries. Hollows may provide habitats for the shelter of foxes, badgers, mice, voles, even of deer, dogs and – as the record tells – occasionally humans. Some hollows may provide seating for a number of people. For example, the Bowthorpe Oak in Lincolnshire, estimated to be over a millennium old, has been fitted with seats which ring its interior, and was once used as the venue for a dinner party after a hunting trip in which Lord Grantham killed a boar reputed to have weighed over a thousand pounds. And as we have already seen, the hollow within a certain yew tree in Sussex, four thousand years old, was sufficiently large to permit the installation of a pub within. In the interiors of trees can be found many things, perhaps even a king, as John Evelyn recounts in his *Sylva*, or perhaps only a persisting vibration or resonance, as a plucked string may continue to move, and this movement be felt, long after it becomes inaudible.

★

Are you oak? Elm, Beech or Horn-Beam? Could you be Ash, Chestnut or Wallnut? What soil is it in which you stand? Might you be Sycomor or Lime-Tree? Do Poplar, Aspen or Abel take your necessary shape? Or are you Quick-Beam, Hasel, Birch or Alder? Would I find you a Withy? Sallow, Ozier, Willow? Weeping or no?

★

I have moved house, out to the edge of the city where the river runs and the sun streams through the trees each morning. The coroner's report is no longer where it was, up above me, on a shelf high up to my left, but down low in the bookshelf behind the door. It took several moments to remember this new location just now, to remember that it still followed me about, was still retrievable, and I cannot deny that this succeeded remembrance engendered a kind of drop, a sagging of the spirit, because perhaps it would be better – easier – if it was lost.

Still I have not found myself capable of reading it. It is like a high leap from one roof to another which my instinct continues to discover is too far for the body to attempt. Don't I know it all anyway, and better? Wouldn't reading it detract from this truth – these truths – which I already know, which are true because they are mine in their own way? What truth can there be left when it is threshed through the categories, definitions and judgements of bureaucratic machinery so that it might reside in lawful words?

I leave it where it is, walk out of the house, down the road, over the river and across the fields along what some committee has agreed to call the Boudicca Way. Perhaps I will see or hear a clutch of dead Roman babies, hear a thundering of hooves. Instead, halfway up a narrow path edged by old twisted hedgebushes I find an oak so hollowed out that it really has no interior at all. It is more like an old gnarled book, foxed and furred at its edges by half a millennium of clinging on, opened up and flattened by time but still managing to support the significant weight of several mighty branches above. And I find I don't think about you – until, by finding this, I do.

*

The manifold dangers to trees: weed, sucker, fern, over-much wet (whether brackish, bitter, stagnant or putrid, sower, acrimonious, vitriolic, arenous and gravelly, churlish, harsh and lean, promiscuously mentioned), bark-binding, multifarious worm, measels, crookedness, excortication, deer, conies, hare, moss, ivy, misselto, fungi, canker, hollowness, hornets and wasps, earwigs and snails, wind-shock, lightning-blast, mice and rats, pismires, rooks, bullfinch, titmouse, excessive cold or heat, cattle and goats whose mouths and breath are poison to trees, you can tell by the horns on them. It is a miracle that any of us may survive the trials of Life.

Against all the many dangers we held before Christianity in our pagan sense the Robigalia in which a dog was sacrificed to appease Robigus, the deity of agricultural disease; and after Pan was exiled and the light of Christ flooded through the woods and over the fields we held our harvest festivals as the pagan days became; and after the greater light of Science eclipsed Him, we had remedies of the spade, till, wand, cudgel, cerecloth, knife, application of loam, the hanging of counterpoises, selective nourishment of a topshoot, anointing with *stercus humanum* – will one's own do? – tempered with water or urine, the stoppering of holes with tar and goosedung, the conveyance of fumes of brimstone into the animals' cells, traps, cow dung, garlic, the juice of rue, decoctions of *colloquintida*, hemp-seed, worm-wood, tobacco, wall-nut-shells, when green, with the leaves of sage, urine and ashes, shooting (of cunning birds), destruction of habitudes (nests), drowning trap, and numerous poisons and injurious concoctions: bane, powder of orpiment in milk, aconites mix'd with butter, green-glass broken with honey, morsels of sponge chopp'd small and fry'd in lard. But some trees cannot be saved, and by mysterious process fade away even as in their size they do not diminish. What can we have now to protect us? How long truly did you hang there from the bough? Have you been there through all time? Who was there at the tree's foot to offer the corpse of the dog against your disease? Might it have worked? You who would not tolerate the hurting of the little animals but rather offer yourself to victual them, Christlike. Did you not take the knife between the ribs as He took the spear? And did then the jackdaw take peck of your most succulent part, the berry of your eye, before you were cut down?

★

I determine again to myself that I will go to the woodland, certainly, yes I will. I will find the farmer who found my brother, and ask him to take me to the place, where the tree stands with the orange cord still looped round the bough, and I will see what the real wood, the real place, much nearer in time also to the day he died at the beginning of May, feels like.

But again instinct comes: No, I will not go.

For so long I have thought about going to the place, and I have imagined that it will be just as I imagine it, and so this will be too hard, because the cord will be there or not there, and the fact of it all will be incontrovertible, inescapable. But that's not actually the trouble at all. The real reason I don't want to go there, I now understand, is that it will not be at all like the woodland I go to in my imagination, that mythic space which childhood memory has made inaccessible to anyone – especially myself – and by that token, the real place will erase the place I go to, and the place which is true will be closed up for good. There will be no more shelter, no more space beyond space, nowhere to stash the meaning and value like clippings of gold coin. Only a mad person would desire to be exiled from a place which loops up time and crosses space and makes death into nothing.

*

Today I feel so very sad to have lost you.

I remember the last time we met, outside the Garnet Wolsey in Norwich. We engaged in the activity of putting four pints of Guinness into our interiors – I probably quoted this at the time – and there was a betterness about him.

A few months before, we had met for the first time in three years, after the death threats and coded messages written and sent in spite against coded messages received and perceived, the whole world war of it all, every message equally empty, senseless, except for the signification they made of a creeping exile from this world. I thought about bringing a knife – or perhaps I did bring a knife, the one with the blade which locks into a curved rosewood handle which I had borrowed from a friend thirty years ago and never given back. Perhaps he did too. The pupils of his eyes had disappeared into pinpricks, just as they used to after the inhalation of two litres of cannabis smoke from a homemade pipe, and there was hardly anyone there at all. And had I known about it then, I would have had to try very hard not to tell him about Fatal Familial Insomnia, which became for a time another obsession of mine, and how the sudden shrinking of the pupils to pinpricks in the individual heralds a period of insomnia, with associated anxiety, hallucination and physiological shutdown, which is untreatable and persists until death, usually between a year and eighteen months after the onset of symptoms. That would have made us laugh.

Emptied out of himself by medication, there was a nothing occurring behind his face, and all I could think of were abandoned houses.

★

Might you speak, as did that other tree, in the best of dreams? Do you hold your bright beams still out in that timeless wood? Did there spring from your bark such blood from the wound of his knife? When I think of solitary you, you are many.

Did Yggdrasil quiver, with you, at the weight of him? Did the nine worlds shake? Did the four stags make bellow at the deathful shiver of it? Did Odin's horsetree make inquiry across the glade, to share stories of the long days and nights beneath his weight? How might himself to himself, and where is the sense in it?

Did Pan come at that time, to caulk his mortality with your saps? Did he tread hooves upon the bunched roots at your foot and make his characteristic chuckle? Did he lay a bouquet of mathematical flowers?

Did they knap flints beneath your spread? Did they feed fire with the storm-lost parts of you? At which bright spark did the gods begin to spring out of your boughs and shape?

Did the springsprung squirrels make tracks about your maypole, over the deep-scarred bark? Did the urging buds know what was gathered in, and how they would burst open, and what now the difference? Do the birds still now sing within you?

Are you everything which they say you are? Which is every possibility, being as you are SIGN? Are you worldtree, everywhere, everyone? What is at your roots? You who connect what is beneath to what is above, what will we do when you are felled?

Is it possible, that where such bad has happened, has happened good?

If it is true, that you are dead at your centre, where then will the words be made? Does what was, become what will be, because of the Tree? When will you speak?

★

'You see,' he began (again the visitor came to rock in his rocking chair over the gravel in the night-time of my back yard), 'the ways of the trees mirror the ways of men. They tremor, breathe, quake and scream. Ignited, wood makes hasty negotiation with the air in the production of flames like men at furious business with capital. And just as it is with people, so too are trees dead at their centres. They only attend to the things around them, the diversions of sensible life, and ignore the growing hollow at the centre where the sound of nothing can never be let to leave.'

He spread a hand, turned it in the air, turned it back, made a slight flicking motion, a practised prestidigitator's trick, and a true flame sprung up at one fingertip, from which he lit his cigarette.

'I have spent so long in the midst of that tree now that the ages have passed. You are aware that none of this is actually here any more, aren't you?'

He planted the cigarette into a long thin holder which looked to be no more than a hollow reed and with the other hand began picking oak leaves, acorns and the odd earwig out from the mess of his hair.

'I became one with the tree, snuck into its Maytime buds, into the tips of its twigs and branches, down along the filaments of its rings, into its saps and waters, the tubers of its roots, into the earth, the nitrogen of me, and now I'm everywhere. I like now nothing more than to sit and dwell on the numbers, think with burrowing thought into the deeps of the numbers, and like a knot of twine or muscle teased with the finger the numbernesses of each number dissipates, and then I can sit and dwell on what the numberness was trying to get at but couldn't, which is the shape of – how-shall-I-say-it – *heaven*, I suppose, if heaven is utter engrossment. Be aware, the world is a deeply boring place. I would recommend that you come and join me, and I know that you have considered it, but I know you won't, because you lack courage, and because it could be no heaven for you, because there's nobody to control.'

He lifted and turned his hand this way and that like a paddle, a paddle for thought and reflection – to think, even, is merely to reflect, which is nothing but the throwing of light back – and it did have the appearance of wood, though raw and unworked, uncut even, tobacco-browned and tipped with long yellow fingernails. Sometimes he liked to make sense, and sometimes he liked to make nonsense, and really it was no different to how it had been when he was alive, because as long as it denied chaos, it was fit and right and good, ah-man.

★

The next night he announced himself by means of a working scale model of the solar system constructed entirely of smoke, and which was given cause to float through my open window and play about the light fitment above the bed.

That is very clever, I said.

I *am* very clever, he replied. But you never wanted to admit it.

That is not true. In fact, it's as untrue as what you said last night about never having derived enjoyment from a bodily existence.

I did not say that. Your problem is that you are *sloppy*. But actually, yes, I was right, especially so if you are saying I was wrong. It is true: my habitation inside a body brought me no pleasure.

I was about to object to this assertion when I noticed that each of the planets of smoke which orbited the smoke sun above me was modelled after a caricature of members of the treble-winning Liverpool Football Club squad of 1984: Ian Rush as Jupiter, Graeme Souness as Saturn, Bruce Grobbelaar as Uranus, Mark Lawrenson as Neptune. I remembered that my brother could be very funny. No sooner had I begun moving from these largest planets inwards, eager to discover who might be identified with the sun, however, than the forms drifted, spun out of shape, their several moons spinning off into that long and silent drift as awaits all things, and the smoke dissipated into the air of the room. I felt a rush of bewilderment and frustration, and then heard a little chuckle from beneath my window.

I rose from the bed and, looking down, watched as he turned his hand again in that paddled way, eyeing it like a blackbird eyes everything (*Come, great dark bird.*) And it was only later that I came to understand that this was goodbye. I have not seen him since.

★

Idly, again, I look a word up, and find that 'brother' exhibits the highest stability of word forms across all the sister languages of Eurasia, and so we see what is true to be true in multiple ways, as it too is multiple, brother upon brother, a shattered mirror, which gives image upon image: from Proto-Indo-European root *bhrater- shoots grew up to Sanskrit *bhrátár-*, Greek *phratér*, Latin *frater* and Proto-Germanic *brothar*, from which, to take only that branch, there sprang Old Norse *bróðir*, Danish *broder*, Old Frisian *brother* and Dutch *broeder;* likewise *bruodar* of Old High German, Gothic *bróþar*, German *Bruder*, the *bropor* of Old English, whence our English *brother*. The brothers of Europe finding in among the misshapen stones of their languages this common rock, and yet: only enmity.

For him to express enthusiasm was not uncommon, but to detect the unmistakable lineaments of joy on his face, this had not been known for many years, not since before the crossing into adulthood, unless, unless –

I have spent many hours going over maps of the Pennines in an attempt to discover the place where I experienced his own experience, a knot in time around which I saw the crystals of pleasure glint. Glint, gleam, glance – these of the *gl-* camp of *shine* words, as went round about the old thatched houses, Germanic as peat and bone – the words spread out with leaves flat from the tree, far, far from their origin at the cracked centre where the fibrousness has grown and the death came to hollow out. It is difficult to experience absolute pleasure with another human with whom one has not prepared the way of it by the sharing of a bed. I cannot find the place on the map. To think back to the experience in three-dimensional space, if that is not an antiquated name for the world which had been around us, the experience of remembering, which is no less than experiencing again, is as unlike as it can be. To look at a map of one's hometown is to be filled with outrage at the lies of the orderers. What? So-and-so Road is parallel to this other? Impossible.

We were cycling from Nottingham to Edinburgh for some reason I cannot remember – in truth, no reason at all; an attempt to have each other as brother.

Somewhere in the Pennines there is a long descent from the heather and gorse of the Peaks down between hunched banks and wire fences tufted with raw wool; a winding mile of road which we took at speed through a still air thus made wind by ourselves, what a roar of impossible friction, down toward the tight and the loose loops at the bottom, past the smeared oblong of a pub, gone, flashings of light, chrome, edge, wire, knives – can the wind be made of knife? – the snare of the telecoms lines eluded again, all shape unshorn and thrown off, uncloaked and unyoked by speed peripherally and centrally through all the body and beyond.

I was stopped at the bottom, my left leg down, and I turned and saw your face as you came down into the vale. What was that? That was joy. And there was no covering it because speed had taken and uncloaked us with a blast, brother wind.

*

The most certain sign of livingness is errancy, a will in the thing living always to become something else, because this is how life is sustained. In a similar way, he, as I, must always remain in movement, striving, because to sit down in a chair and cease into ease is a kind of sin against the movingness of all being. (Even in a sitting pebble the molecules make tiny thrum.) Likewise with signs, which demonstrate an urge to be nosing about continually in the depths of meaning and popping up like rabbits in quite unexpected burrows, far removed from the hole they went in.

Just as the Thames made new banks for the shifting sea, as the White Horse's grooms dug deep to make that absence of earth;

as those garlanded with oak leaves made fearful pledge to their gods, sometimes meek, sometimes wroth; just as the poet spoke out the voice of the Tree in praise of what would be; just as all of these, so I, this, to you.

And so, when the day came, I did in fact go to the tree, and found myself there in this corporeal form, human, though of course much other besides, put together out of compounds and chemicals, processes and transformations, the passages and crossings of wondrous metabolisation. And so I hunkered down to the roots of him, and – all things that are, having the capacity to become other – I made good nitrogen food of myself, and bubbled down into the roots of him, deep to the very hair-ends of the roots of him, where I could be taken in and give succour to the tree. Up through the fibrous stems I went; up, up the twisted roots, past the bole, into the trunk, beneath the bark and cambium – harken to my woody progress and the sound of it, the resonance of the particular tree of him – up, up the heart and sapwood I went, and I was many'd out into the branches, and the goodness of me ran along them, dividing and subdividing, until I came to the buds and the leaves of him, where the life is, but where also it ends, where the mystery of it all resides, and trees it is hard to contemplate so new with the world, sporous Archaeopteris standing before all others a mere three hundred and fifty million years since, and I feed and fed him, and will continue to, until it's my turn to become my own tree out there where time ends, or begins.

Acknowledgements

Photograph of the old Devizes White Horse reproduced with the kind permission of the Jean Morrison Collection at the Wiltshire and Swindon History Centre.

Images of graffiti in the Stoke-by-Clare church reproduced with kind permission of the Norfolk and Suffolk Medieval Graffiti Surveys.

Image of the moon graben reproduced from a photograph taken by Apollo 10 for NASA.

Image of a printed page of mathematics from Paul Glendinning's *Stability, Instability and Chaos: An Introduction to the Theory of Nonlinear Differential Equations* (Cambridge University Press, 1994).

Image of Mark's signature across the title page of Morris Kline, *Mathematical Thought from Ancient to Modern Times* (Oxford University Press, 1990).

Image of foetus *in fetu* from Nisreen M. Khalifa, Doaa W. Maximous and Alla A. Abd-Elsayed, 'Fetus in Fetu: A Case Report', *Journal of Medical Case Reports*, no. 2: 2008.

Image of W. G. Sebald's memorial on the grounds of the University of East Anglia reproduced courtesy of Richard Hibbitt.

Quotations from Rousseau from Jean-Jacques Rousseau, *The Confessions*, translated by J. M. Cohen (London: Penguin, 1953).

Quotations relating to the voyage of the Trieste bathyscaphe from J. Piccard and R. S. Dietz, *Seven Miles Down: The Story of the Bathyscaph Trieste* (Putnam: New York, 1961).

Quotations from the Hávamál translated by Carolyne Larrington in *The Poetic Edda* (Oxford World's Classics, 1999).

Rom Houben, as represented by Linda Wouters, quoted from an article by Manfred Dworschak published 25 November 2009 in Spiegel.de.

Quotation from W. G. Sebald's *Unerzählt*, translated by Michael Hamburger as *Unrecounted* (Penguin: London, 2005).

GALLEY BEGGAR PRESS

We hope that you've enjoyed *My Mind to Me a Kingdom Is*. If you would like to find out more about Paul, along with some of his fellow authors, head to www.galleybeggar.co.uk.

There, you will also find information about our subscription scheme, 'Galley Buddies', which is there to ensure we can continue to put out ambitious and unusual books like *My Mind to Me a Kingdom Is*.

Subscribers to Galley Beggar Press:

· receive limited black-cover editions of our future titles (printed in a one-time run of 600).

· have their names included in a special acknowledgement section at the back of our books.

· are sent regular updates and invitations to our book launches, talks and other events.

· enjoy a 20% discount code for the purchase of any of our backlist (as well as for general use throughout our online shop).

WHY BE A GALLEY BUDDY?

At Galley Beggar Press we don't want to compromise on the excellence of the writing we put out, or the physical quality of our books. We've also enjoyed numerous successes and prize nominations since we set up in 2012. Almost all of our authors have gone on to be longlisted, shortlisted, or the winners of over twenty of the world's most prestigious literary awards.

But publishing for the sake of art is a risky commercial strategy. In order to keep putting out the very best books we can, and to continue to support talented writers, we need your help. The money we receive from our Galley Buddy scheme is an essential part of keeping us going.

By becoming a Galley Buddy, you help us to launch and foster a new generation of writers.

To join today, head to:
https://www.galleybeggar.co.uk/subscribe

FRIENDS OF GALLEY BEGGAR PRESS

Galley Beggar Press would like to thank the following individuals, without the generous support of whom our books would not be possible:

Cameron Adams
Muriel Adams
Kémy Ade
Timothy Ahern
Liz Aiken
Sam Ainsworth
Jez Aitchison
Richard Allen
Lulu Allison
Adrian Alvarez
Anna Andreou
Simon Andrup
Jerome Anello
Kirk Annett
Deborah Arata
Robert Armiger
Sean Arnold
Curt Arnson
Jake Arthur
Xanthe Ashburner
Bethany Ashley
Robert Ashton
Edmund Attrill
Valda Aviks
Jo Ayoubi
Kerim Aytec
Claire Back
Thomas Badyna
Andrew Bailey
Dexter Bailey
Tom Bailey
Edward Baines
Glynis Baker
James Baker
Maggie Balistreri
Sarah Balstrup
Paul Bangert
Victoria Barkas
Andrea Barlien
Chad Barnes

Matthew Barron
Phil Bartlett
Morgan Baxley
Rachael Beale
Rebecca Bealey
James Beavis
Rachel Bedder
Joseph Bell
Angel Belsey
Madeline Bennett
Felicity Bentham
Jean Bergin
Michelle Best
Gary Betts
David Bevan
Allison Beynon
Alison Bianchi
Gavin Bingham
Sandra Birnie
Donna-Louise Bishop
Mark Blackburn
Peter Blackett
Matt Blackstock
Kate Bland
Melissa Blaschke
Charlie Bloor
Lynne Blundell
David Boddy
Sophie Boden
Rich Boden
John Bogg
Poppy Boutell
Edwina Bowen
Gemma Bowles
Michelle Bowles
Joanna Bowman
Alexander Bown
Matthew Boyd
David Bradley
Sean Bradley

David Brady
Andrew Bremner
Joan Brennan
Chris Brewer
Amanda Bringans
Erin Britton
Julia Brocking
Anthony Brown
Dean Brooks
Lily Brown
Peter Brown
Sheila Browse
Carrie Brunt
David Bruson
Richard Bryant
Lesley Budge
Daniel Bugg
Laura Bui
Gayle Burgoyne
Tony Burke
Kevin Burrell
Tamsin Bury
Esther van Buul
Sarah Brayshaw
Andrew Bremner
Kester Brewin
Barry Bryne
Barbara Byar
Alan Calder
June Caldwell
Matt Callow
Francesca
    Cambridge Mallen
Mark Campbell
Laura Canning
Annette Capel
Rhian Capener
Andrew Cardus
Ros Carne
Jackie Carpenter

Leona Carpenter
Daniel Carr
Sean Carroll
Shaun Carter
Stuart Carter
Liam Casey
David Caves
Leigh Chambers
Sonja Chander
Richard Chatterton
Christel Chen
Lina Christopoulou
Neal Chuang
Gemma Church
Neil Churchill
Jack Clark
Deborah Ann Clarke
Simon Clarke
Douglas
   Clarke-Williams
Steve Clough
Steven Coghill
Paul Cole
Faith Coles
John Coles
Emma Coley
Sam Coley
Christine Collings
X Collins
Jess Conway
Joe Cooney
Sarah Corbett
Sarah Corrie
Paul Corry
Andy Corsham
Mary Costello
Sally Cott
Nick Coupe
Diarmuid Cowan
Isabelle Coy-Dibley
Matthew Craig
Anne Craven
Anne-Marie Creamer
Alan Crilly
Joanna Crispin
Brenda Croskery
Alasdair Cross
James Cross
Jenny Crossland

Kate Crowcroft
Miles Crowley
Stephen Cuckney
John Cullinane
Damian Cummings
Stephen Cummins
Andrew Cupples
TR Currell
Patrick Curry
Emma Curtis Lake
Chris Cusack
Will Dady
Siddharth Dalal
Rupert Dastur
Sally Davenport
Claudia Daventry
Andrew Davies
Julie Davies
Linda Davies
Nickey Davies
Ian Daw
Emilie Day
Emily Day
Toby Day
Sarah Deacon
Ann Debono
Meaghan Delahunt
Rebecca Demeree
Stanislaus Dempsey
Paul Dettmann
Angelica Diehn
Jane Dietrich
Kasper Dijk
Turner Docherty
William Dobson
Mark Dolan
Dennis Donothan
Kirsty Doole
Oliver Dorostkar
David Douce
Janet Dowling
Kelly Downey
Jamie Downs
Alan Duckers
Ian Dudley
Fiona Duffy
Anthony Duncan
Stanka Easton
Matthew Eatough

Nicola Edwards
Lance Ehrman
Jonathan Elkon
Ian Ellison
Thomas Ellmer
Theresa Emig
Stefan Erhardt
Fiona Erskine
Frances Evangelista
Gareth Evans
Kieran Evans
Adam Fales
Sarah Farley
Pauline Farrar
Emma Feather
Lori Feathers
Gerard Feehily
Jeremy Felt
Victoria Fendall
Maria Guilliana Fenech
Michael Fenton
Edward J. Field
Paul Fielder
Catriona Firth
Becky Fisher
Duncan Fisher
Nicholas Fisher
Mark Flaum
Alexander Fleming
Grace
   Fletcher-Hackwood
Hayley Flockhart
Nicholas Flower
Patrick Foley
James Fourniere
Ceriel Fousert
Richard Fradgley
Matthew Francis
Nigel Francis
Bridget Fraser
Emily Fraser
Emma French
Ruth Frendo
Elizabeth Frye
Melissa Fu
Graham Fulcher
Paul Fulcher
Michael Furness
John Gallagher

Timothy Gallimore
Marc Galvin
Annabel Gaskell
Nolan Geoghegan
Phil Gibby
Alison Gibson
Luke Gibson
Jacqueline Gittens
James Goddard
Stephanie Golding
Elizabeth Goldman
Morgan Golf-French
Sakura Gooneratne
Sara Gore
Nikheel Gorolay
Cathy Goudie
Simon Goudie
Emily Grabham
Judith Griffith
Ben Griffiths
Neil Griffiths
Vicki Grimshaw
Christopher Gruppet
Sam Gugliani
Robbie Guillory
Andrew Gummerson
Dave Gunning
Ian Hagues
Daniel Hahn
Callum Hale-Thomson
Nikki Hall
Alice Halliday
Verity Halliday
Peter Halliwell
Emma Hammond
Paul Handley
Rachel Handley
Paul Hanson
Jill Harrison
Greg Harrowing
Alice Harvey
Becky Harvey
Espen Hauglid
Simon Hawkesworth
Connor Hayden
Adrian Hayes
Rachel Heath
David Hebblethwaite
Richard Hemmings

Peter Hemsworth
Petra Hendrickson
Padraig J. Heneghan
Stu Hennigan
Adam Saiz Abo
   Henriksen
Penelope
   Hewett-Brown
Felix Hewison-Carter
Simon Higgins
Annette Higgs
Alexander Highfield
Jennifer Hill
Daniel Hillman
David Hirons
Ned Hirst
Marcus Hobson
Jamie Hodder-Williams
Nicholas Hodges
Stephenjohn Holgate
Turan Holland
Aisling Holling
Ben Holloway
Adrian Howe
Steve Hubbard
Hugh Hudson
Anna Jean Hughes
Emily Hughes
Richard Hughes
Robert Hughes
Jon Hulbert
Kim-ling Humphrey
Joanne Humphries
Louise Hussey
LJ Hutchins
William Hsieh
Lori Inglis Hall
Simon Issatt
Joseph Jackson
Ryan Jackson
Jane Jakeman
Briley James
Hayley James
Helen James
Michael James
Graeme Jarvie
Kavita A. Jindal
Rachel John
Alex Jones

Bevan Jones
Deborah Jones
Ellen Jones
Jupiter Jones
Rebecca Jones
Amy Jordison
Anna Jordison
Diana Jordison
Atul Joshi
Sapna Joshi
Claire Jost
Benjamin Judge
Gary Kaill
Darren Kane
Thomas Kealy
Andrew Kelly
Michael Ketchum
Jeffrey Kichen
Anna Kime
Xanath King
Clara Knight
Jacqueline Knott
Amy Koheealiee
David Krakhauer
Emily Kubisiak
Elisabeth Kumar
Rachel Lalchan
Philip Lane
Dominique
   Lane-Osherov
I Lang
Kathy Lanzarotti
Kim Laramee
Steven Law
Jo Lawrence
Lorraine Lawrence
Andrew
   Lawton-Collins
Sue Lawson
Elizabeth Leach
Stephen Leach
Rick Le Coyte
Jessica Leggett
Carley Lee
Liz and Pete Lee
Edwin Lerner
Chiara Levorato
Sara Levy
Elizabeth Leyland

Oliver Lewis
Yin Lim
Chris Lintott
Clayton Lister
Amy Lloyd
Lyn Lockwood
Katie Long
Tracey Longworth
Nikyta Loraine
Zoe Lourie
Kathryn Lovell
Lele Lucas
John Lutz
Michael Lynch
Marc Lyth
Paul McAuley
James McCann
Leona McCann
Amy McCauley
Lucie McKnight Hardy
Chris McLaren
Paul McCombs
Fabia McDougall
Grace McHale
Sheila McIntosh
Alan McIntyre
Eleanor McIntyre
Sarah McIntyre
Victoria MacKenzie
Duncan Mackie
Gerald McWilliams
Brendan Madden
Joseph Maffey
Anne Maguire
Eleanor Maier
Johnny Mains
Philip Makatrewicz
Sarah Male
Anil Malhotra
Tom Mandall
Joshua Mandel
Venetia Manning
Chiara Margiotta
John Marr
Natalie Marshall
Paul Marshall
Aoife Martin
Iain Martin
William Mascioli

Rachel Mason
Rebecca Masterman
Susan Maxwell
Dan Mayers
Stephen Maynard
Sally Mayor
Jason Merrells
Andy Merrills
Tina Meyer
Lindsey Millen
Michael Millington
Ali Millar
Phillipa Mills
Robert Mills
Sally Minogue
Fiona Mitchell
Lindsay Mitchell
Ian Mond
Fiona Mongredien
Alexander Monker
Alex Moore
Clare Moore
Gary Moore
Michelle Moorhouse
Jonathan Moreland
Nigel J. Morgan
Carlos Eduardo Morreo
Catriona Morris
Jackie Morris
Joanne Morris
Julie Morris
Patrick Morris
Clive Morrison
Donald Morrison
Roger Morrison
Harriet Mossop
Jennifer Mulholland
Christian Murphy
Ben Myers
Electra Nanou
Linda Nathan
Tim Neighbour
Marie Laure Neulet
Natalie Newman
Amanda Nicholls
Catherine Nicholson
Sophia Nixon
Mariah de Nor
Emma Norman

Sam North
Calum Novak-
 Mitchell
Anna Nsubuga
Arif Nurmohamed
Simon Nurse
Rachel Nye
Christopher O'Brian
James O'Brien
Rodney O'Connor
James O'Leary
Alec Olsen
Valerie O'Riordan
Sam Osborne
Liz O'Sullivan
Kate Packwood
Dave Parry
Simon Parsons
Gary Partington
Debra Patek
Ian Patterson
Adam Paxton
Mark Payne
Stephen Pearsall
Rosie Pendlebury
Jonathan Perks
Davide Perottoni
Connor Perrie
Tom Perrin
Seetal Petal
Tony Pettigrew
Dan Phillips
Fergus Pickles
Hannah Piekarz
Steven Pilling
Robert Pisani
Ben Plouviez
Louise Pointer
Alex Pointon
 Melville
Dimitrios Polemis
Erin Polmear
James Pomar
Jonathan Pool
Christopher Potter
Lesley Preston
Libby Preston
David Prince
Victoria Proctor

Jill Propst
James Puddephatt
Alan Pulverness
Lisa Quattromini
Leng Leng Quek
Zoe Radley
Jane Rainbow
Sim Ralph
Polly Randall
Lauren Razavi
Ian Redfern
Sam Reese
Padraid Reidy
Vasco Resende
Amy Reynolds
Caroline Riddell
Mario Riggio
Alison Riley
Thea Marie Rishovd
Laura Roach
Chris Roberts
Stephen Roberts
Emily Robinsonb
Joanna Robinson
Joyce Lillie Robinson
Rocky and Kat
Lizz Roe
Lorraine Rogerson
Kalina Rose
Michael Rowley
Nathan Rowley
Martin Rowsell
Beverly Rudy
Giles Ruffer
Naben Ruthnum
John Rutter
Paul Ryan
Amanda Saint
Floriane Sajdak
Alison Sakai
Himanshu Kamal Saliya
Robert Sanderson
Benedict Sangster
Steven Saville
Lior Sayada
Liam Scallon
Amy Scarrott
Linde Schaafsma
Robert Scheffel

Benedict Schofield
Jan Schoones
Ros Schwartz
Nicola Scott
Stephen Robert Scott
Darren Seeley
Darren Semple
Elie Sharp
Nicola Shepherd
Emma Shore
Elena Shushakova
Deborah Siddoway
Kate Simpson
Stu Sizer
Ann Slack
Mark Slater
Jay Slayton-Josh
Ben Smith
Catherine Smith
Chris Smith
Hazel Smith
Helen Smith
Ian Smith
Kieron Smith
Nicola Smith
Shannon Smith
Tom Smyth
Haydon Speenceley
Arabella Spencer
Sarah Spitz
S.O. Spitzer
Chiara Spruijt
Levi Stahl
Conor Stait
Karl Stange
Daniel Staniforth
Cameron Stark
Cathryn Steele
Gillian Stern
Jack Stevens
Zac Stevens
Mark Stevenson
Jow Stewart
Dagmara Stoic
Jamie Stone
Justina Stonyte
Anne Storr
Elizabeth Stott
Julia Stringwell

Andrew Stuart
Daryl Sullivan
Jesse Surridge
Drashti Sutariya
Helen Swain
Ashley Tame
Sarah Tapp
Ednyfed Tappy
Justine Taylor
Peter Taylor
Moray Teale
Alan Teder
Gill Thackray
Helen Thain
Darren Theakstone
Cennin Thomas
Sue Thomas
Susannah Thompson
Julian Thorne
Matthew Thrift
Matthew Tilt
Amie Tolson
James Torrance
Eloise Touni
Kate Triggs
Stefani Tuirigangi
Jojo Tulloh
Steve Tuffnell
Davon Tupper
Eleanor Updegraff
Geoffrey Urland
Raminta Uselyte
Francesca Veneziano
Irene Verdiesen
Julia Wait
Chris Walker
Craig Walker
Phoebe Walker
Stephen Walker
Ben Waller
Sinead Walsh
Steve Walsh
Zhen Wang
Jerry Ward
Kate Ward
Peter Ward
Rachael Wardell
Guy Ware
Darren Waring

Diane Waring
Emma Warnock
Stephanie Wasek
Daniel Waterfield
Sarah Webb
Ian Webster
Lucy Webster
Adam Welch
Joanna Wellings
Karl Ruben Weseth
Jo West-Moore
Wendy Whidden
Robert White

Ben Wilder
Kyra Wilder
Claire Willerton
G Williams
Sharon Williams
Sarah Wiltshire
Kyle Winkler
Bianca Winter
Lucie Winter
Sheena Winter
Astrid Maria
   Wissenburg
Stephen Witkowski

Michael Wohl
Nathan Wood
Sarah Wood
Paul Woodgate
Emma Woolerton
Lorna Wright
Faye Young
Ian Young
Juliano Zaffino
Vanessa Zampiga
Sylvie Zannier
Rupert Ziziros
Carsten Zwaaneveld